D1042231

INDIVIDUALIZATION
OF INSTRUCTION

INDIVIDUALIZATION OF INSTRUCTION

A Teaching Strategy

Virgil M. Howes

International Center for
Educational Development

THE MACMILLAN COMPANY
COLLIER-MACMILLAN LIMITED, LONDON

Copyright © 1970, Virgil M. Howes

Printed in the United States of America

All rights reserved. No part of this book may be reproduced or transmitted in any form or by any means, electronic or mechanical, including photocopying, recording, or any information storage and retrieval system, without permission in writing from the Publisher.

The Macmillan Company
866 Third Avenue, New York, New York, 10022

Collier-Macmillan Canada, Ltd., Toronto, Ontario

Library of Congress catalog card number: 72–92082

First Printing

PREFACE

Individualization of instruction is something to advocate, to champion, and to be in favor of, even if what it means is not clear. It is popular as it has been in the past and yet there is promise that a fuller understanding and meaning is evolving this "second time around."

Today, individualization of instruction is one of the most important directions for innovation and reform in American education. The search for meaning and practice is both a major and a serious one. Writings exploring the concept and its application in the educational enterprise continue to mount. Workshops, institutes, and conferences focus on it as a theme. As attempts are made to open one door of the concept, another awaits to be opened, and so the pattern goes.

The movement from a group-oriented, teacher-directed, instructional strategy to an individualized-personalized strategy is a fundamental redesigning of numerous components of the instructional process. Implementation in the classroom will vary according to the perceptions teachers have of the concept. What is the role of the teacher? Of the pupil? How shall the classroom be organized? What management procedures are needed? Who decides what? Should pupils select their learning materials? Make choices of what is to be learned? How can I find the time to individualize? Won't I need group work? How do I start? What material will I need? These and hosts of other questions are raised as teachers, school faculties, and administrators begin a thoughtful dialogue on individualization of instruction and practices for implementation.

Answers are varied because individualization of instruction is a way of thinking about the teaching-learning process. It is an attitude toward the function of the school, a broader way of thinking about class organization, materials, and the approach to the individual child. It demands a new conception of a curriculum.

It is, then, to assist the reader to deal with these questions, to formulate a clearer understanding of the concept, that these volumes have been developed. This volume explores **individualization** from the viewpoint of a general teaching strategy. Readings have been selected which discuss the way of individualization, the what, and the how. In the second volume, **individualization** is viewed in terms of program and practices in social studies, reading, and the language arts. Material for a third volume is focused on science, mathematics, and the general area of computer-assisted instruction.

The rigororous search for materials included a review of numerous professional journals starting from 1960, curriculum bulletins, and other publications by district and county offices, as well as addresses and material prepared for workshops and conferences on the theme. Because the purpose of these readings is to assist teachers and administrators working as school faculties and students preparing to be teachers, selections were limited to those that explore the concept of individualization in what was felt to be the most significant in terms of classroom application and day-to-day school operation.

To the authors and publishers whose material appears in this book, my deepest thanks for their graciousness and willingness in granting permission. To William Michael Martin for his assistance in searching out material for these volumes, and to Miss Sheila Dyen for her assistance in obtaining permissions and keeping track of the innumerable odds and ends in such a production, I wish to express a special word of appreciation. Without cooperation from these contributors, this work would not have been possible.

V. M. H.

CONTENTS

vii

PART I

Why Individualize?

> Education can have no ends beyond itself. Its value derives from principles and standards implicit in it. To be educated is not to have arrived at a destination; it is to travel with a different view. What is required is not feverish preparation for something that lies ahead, but to work with a precision, possession, and taste at worthwhile things that lie to hand.
>
> R. S. Peters [1]

Aims and purposes are focal points for deliberate and searching discussions if operational practices in the school are to have meaning and value. The concerns, the issues, and the questions which emerge and develop begin to set the stage for operational answers related to individualization of instruction.

What kind of person is to emerge from the school? What is the school for? What is to be learned in the school? What will be learning objectives? What is the role of the learner in decisions about his learning? These and other such questions are more than incidental to any disciplined discussion of individualized instruction. They become the heart of productive dialogue.

[1] "Education as Initiation," *Philosophical Analysis and Education*, ed. by Reginald D. Archambault (New York: The Humanities Press, 1965), p. 107.

1

AN OVERVIEW:
TOWARD THE
INDIVIDUALIZATION
OF INSTRUCTION

Virgil M. Howes

*If we can't teach every student . . . something we
don't know in some form, we haven't a hope of
educating the next generation, because what they
are going to need is what we don't know.*

Margaret Mead [1]

Sputnik of that yesteryear has been a point from which
much in education has been reckoned. Before Sputnik and
after Sputnik have become standard vantage points from
which to view educational reform and change. In the age of
Sputnik, education responded to the authentic voice of mod-
eration and evolutionary change. The curriculum was updated, new architectural forms were explored, instructional
methods and other ways to organize pupils and teachers
served as focuses for field experiments.

But we've passed the Age of Sputnik. And as significant as
those few years were for education, a new age is dawning
which demands more. In the later 60's we saw the beginnings
of revolt sweeping across the world—revolt against power,

[1] Margaret Mead, "Changing Teachers in a Changing World," *The
Education of Teachers: New Perspectives,* Official Report of the
Second Bowling Green Conference, National Commission on Teacher
Education and Professional Standards, NEA (1958), pp. 121–134.

against authority, against institutions, against the Protestant ethic, against "the system." In our own country, the individuality after which we have aspired has become inundated by the triumphs of technology and production. Numbers are replacing names of people, of geographic areas, until the individual is identifiable as this seven digit, that five digit, or some other series of numerals. Increasingly, we find ourselves frustrated and dehumanized and even arguing with machines which mixed a number and notified us of an overdrawn account which was not.

Change, a characteristic of our world, proceeds at a dizzying pace. Technological and scientific achievements, whether they be in space or elsewhere, are helping us to embark on one of the greatest, if not the greatest, age of exploration and discovery mankind has ever known. "In fact," Toffler states, "there is a growing body of reputable opinion that the period we are now living through represents nothing less than the second great divide in human history, comparable in magnitude only with that first great break on historic continuity, the shift from barbarism to civilization." [2]

And there are students protesting. Dissent from the college is moving down and down through the grades. There is increased dissatisfaction with school which first and last places its reliance on order, on futuristic aims resting on answers provided by the past, on content based on knowledge which becomes obsolete almost at the point of attainment, upon guidelines and matching dictates which have an inhuman and forced-feeding quality. More and more school has become a creeping glacier, cold and distant from those it was designed to serve. And students are rebelling, or is it a search for ways to participate in decisions about their own life? Is it any wonder they resent the tyranny of an irrelevant curriculum and training for things that will never be?

What is to be the model for a generation that will walk through doors which before were either locked or unknown?

[2] Alvin Toffler, "The Future as a Way of Life," *Horizon*, Vol. 7 (Summer 1965), pp. 108–115.

There will be more time to think and to feel. There will be more time for pleasure. Time will be a resource and a tool to build knowledge, experience, and the qualities of humanness. Certainly, the focus on schooling as training for a future life of work is inadequate. The essentials today may be notes for history tomorrow. The separation of work and play as opposites must go. Many of our beliefs and values have run their course and are no longer organizing principles around which school can be built.

Schooling must become more than a launching pad for tomorrow. Somehow, it must be good while it's going on. Learning how to learn must overshadow the acquisition of methods, skills, knowledge. Processes by which new problems are met are more relevant than answers from the past. Schools must be thought of as learning centers, not teaching centers. They must become places where one goes to have experiences, where there are opportunities for the young to find their way. Schools have a function and teachers a task—to provide meaningful opportunities for active student participation in the spectrum of learning decisions in a nurturing, sustaining environment designed to foster personal autonomy.

The barricade of fear that children are somehow beasts who need control must be torn down. Modern psychology and medicine tell us that the basic striving in humans is toward health, both physical and mental. As many writers have pointed out, the organism is not our enemy. The child wants the same things we do—the achievement of adequacy. If, then, we prefer to develop flexible, adapting, creative individuals who can meet the continuing challenge of change, we have some beginning knowledge on how to do this. We could establish in our classrooms the conditions and psychological climate which as Rogers has so aptly stated would initiate a process of learning to be free. The choice is ours. For the teacher, the interacting adult with children in the setting of the school, a teaching strategy of individualization or personalized instruction is a beginning in the redirection of education.

WHY INDIVIDUALIZE INSTRUCTION?

Robert E. Keuscher

Human beings are not alike. Their differences are real, inevitable, more subtle and more numerous than we often recognize, and essential to the very survival of the human race. With all due respect to the authors of the American Declaration of Independence, men are actually created different and unequal. As Max Lerner once observed, "this is a fact that every parent knows, every teacher knows, every employer knows, every American knows."

Biologists have confirmed the fact that individuals are not alike, and have demonstrated that differences are essential for the perpetuation of the species. They have shown that uniformity prevents the appearance and evolution of those qualities and attributes necessary for adaptation to the environment and can result in biological extinction. Born different, children are reared differently in a great variety of home environments. They come to school with extremely divergent behavior patterns, interests, attitudes, and levels of readiness for formal learning.

Educators have several alternatives for dealing with variability. They can ignore individual differences—deny they exist; they can tolerate them as a nuisance and a liability; they can attempt to eradicate them and try to get all pupils to conform to some arbitrary standard; or they can cultivate and nurture differences as an asset and precious resource.

In a democratic nation like ours, where a compelling force

Adapted and reprinted from *Individualization of Instruction: A Search*, Los Angeles, California [ASUCLA Students' Store, 308 Westwood Plaza], 1967, pp. 10–29, with the permission of Robert Keuscher.

behind universal free public education has been the concept of an intelligent, enlightened electorate, schools have a responsibility to the society that created them. Educators in the United States have a clear-cut role delineated for them, and it calls for curricular patterns, programs of study, and methods of instruction geared to the needs, interests, and capacities of individuals. Most school personnel admit this responsibility and subscribe to it; in fact, one would be hard put to find a statement of educational aims and purposes which doesn't envision the "development of the individual to his fullest capability." Unfortunately, much more lip service than implementation is given to *individualizing* education. In fact, it is quite safe to say that nothing is more discussed, yet has less done about it than individualization of instruction.

Why individualize? There are a number of compelling reasons why instruction MUST be individualized:

I. Philosophically it is consistent with the principles upon which our form of government, which spawned our educational system, is based.

II. The very nature of our democratic system and the way it functions demands knowledgeable, thinking participants.

III. Assembly line methods are tending to produce mass-produced, standardized citizens at the expense of individuality.

IV. As society grows increasingly complex there is a greater demand for a diversity of talents and skills.

V. It is probably the most efficient way to educate if one focuses on the product rather than just the process.

In this paper we will, first, examine each of these reasons on their own merits; then we will attempt to assess what the schools are doing to individualize instruction today; and finally, we will make some recommendations as to what schools should be doing.

INDIVIDUALIZED INSTRUCTION IS
MORE DEMOCRATIC

From its earliest beginnings, concern for and commitment to the individual have been central themes in the creation and development of this republic. The instigators of the American Revolution and the authors of the Declaration of Independence and the Bill of Rights were motivated by the doctrine of individualism which regards individuals—independent, equal before the law, free to do as they see fit—as the ultimate political units. "Concern with the individual," states President David D. Henry, (1)[1] of the University of Illinois, "has been the theme of our poets and philosophers, the recurring and dominant note in political, religious, social, economic, and cultural history of our nation." The authors of *A Climate for Individuality*, publication of the Joint Project on the Individual and the School, (2) make the flat statement: "The foundation of our nation is its supreme commitment to the individual human being." And the Rockefeller Panel Report, *The Pursuit of Excellence*, (3) takes a similar stand: "The greatness of a nation may be manifested in many ways—in its purposes, its courage, its moral responsibility, its cultural and scientific eminence, the tenor of its daily life. But ultimately, the source of its greatness is in the individuals who constitute the living substance of the nation."

While we have veered dramatically at times in our interpretation of what individualism means—the laissez-faire economic policies of the late 1800's, lethargy in civil rights legislation for the Negro, and justification, on occasion, of either extreme liberalism or extreme conservatism in politics— the ideal is still as appealing philosophically as it ever was. The individual and his rights and privileges are of paramount concern in our democracy.

The federal government in recent years has dramatically

---

[1] Numbers in parentheses refer to references at end of chapter.

reaffirmed its interest in protecting the rights of individuals. The school prayer decision, reversal of the "separate but equal" doctrine in the racial segregation issue, the "one man— one vote" decisions requiring reapportionment of state legislatures, and the Gideon and Escobedo cases redefining the individual's rights before state courts, are only a few significant cases which indicate continued national concern for the individual.

America's true greatness doesn't lie in military might, industrial productivity, or advances in space, no matter how spectacular they may be. The ideal which has made American citizenship the envy of the world is the ideal which proclaims the dignity and worth of the individual person. From our earliest beginnings, our deepest convictions, our highest ideals have cloaked the individual with worth and dignity, recognized his potentialities, and encouraged him to demonstrate his initiative and to unloose his creative powers. These were the ideals that formed the platforms of Jefferson, Wilson, and John F. Kennedy.

INDIVIDUALIZED INSTRUCTION TEACHES CRITICAL THINKING

In a democratic society, formal education must do more than transmit the culture. Citizens must be able to think for themselves, willing to question, and to dissent. Different points of view are an absolute necessity in a nation such as ours, for this is the only climate in which democracy can survive.

Students must be encouraged to question, to criticize, and to argue their point of view. Schools must permit pupils to make choices and to take the responsibility for those choices. Boys and girls must be allowed the experience of making the wrong decisions on occasion and learn to live with the consequences. Students who have had everything decided for them —including what the right answer should be or that which they are expected to "discover"—will not be able to bring themselves to making decisions as adults, let alone making good decisions or accepting the responsibility for them. A vital, dynamic society needs people who dare to be different, people who will assert themselves, lead, experiment, change.

INDIVIDUALIZED INSTRUCTION TEACHES SELF-DIRECTION

The explosion of knowledge and the quickening pace of technological advances make it imperative that schools turn out citizens capable of independent action, self-direction, self-propulsion. This underscores the idea that we cannot and should not feed pupils the same educational diet.

Unfortunately, there is evidence that we are drifting toward impersonality in almost every sphere of our culture, and schooling is not exempt from this trend. Individuality is tending to be submerged in gigantic organizations, assembly line production, standardized procedures, computerized personnel programs, mass propaganda, consensus, and conformity.

Erich Fromm, David Riesman, William H. Whyte, Jr., Norman Friedman, and Arthur Combs are some of the prominent Americans who have spoken out against the present trend. Fromm, author of *Man for Himself*, (4) thinks men should "cultivate themselves" and deplores the fact that such anonymous authorities as "public opinion" and "common sense" are so powerful that we are fearful of being different and so easily led to conform.

Riesman (5) speaks of the need for "autonomous man" and "heightened self-consciousness" and decries "the other-directed fellow." His "inner-directed man" is self-reliant and self-made—the rugged individual.

Whyte (6) argues that men should assert themselves, lead, and be effective. He deplores "human engineering" and man's being "imprisoned by brotherhood." Whyte fears that individuality is being submerged by gigantic organizations and their impersonal methods of operation.

Friedman, in "The Schools and the Defeat of the Child," (7) points out that a democratic society calls for inventiveness and creativity while a commercial society calls for passivity and punctuality. He feels we are fast becoming a vast industrial-commercial machine whose demands run counter to our original democratic ideals and dominate our lives. We can't stop the machine, because we have become entranced by man's age-old dream of material comfort and security which now seems within our grasp through modern technology. Our demand for a higher and higher standard of living is the fuel which keeps the machine going at an ever-increasing pace. Unfortunately, Friedman says, we pay homage to such ideas as freedom, individuality, and variety while increasingly living the lives of, and encouraging our children to live the lives of, sheep.

INDIVIDUALIZED INSTRUCTION NURTURES CREATIVITY

Tyler and Brownell (8) have pointed out that variability in talents, abilities, and temperaments have been recognized in all societies throughout history, and while individual differences are desirable in any culture, widely divergent skills, capacities, and competencies are especially essential in a society as complex as ours. In fact, nurturing individuality, diversity, and creativity may well be the key to maintaining a nation founded on the values which are basic to our republic.

Most of the participants in an interdisciplinary symposia (9) on creativity at Michigan State University, including Fromm, Carl Rogers, Rollo May, and Abraham Maslow, mentioned both a social and an individual need for creativity in this country. They saw the need as a desperate situation, bordering on a national crisis, affecting industry, the military, and humanitarian living. Seemingly, American schools need to promote ingenuity, initiative, and creativity if we are to maintain both our high standard of living and our economic supremacy in the world.

Rogers (10) pointed out the extreme importance of nurturing individuality and creativity when he insisted that our culture is doomed unless individuals and groups alike find new, imaginative ways of adjusting to complex change and the incredible expansion of knowledge, discovery, and inventions. Not only individual maladjustments and group tensions, but eventual international annihilation, will be the price we must pay, Rogers insists, unless man can learn to make adaptations to his environment as rapidly as science is able to change the environment.

Schools have an obligation to encourage pupils to have new ideas, experiment, and innovate. Victor Lowenfeld (11) feels that children now in elementary schools will be asked to revise, change, and remake our world into an entirely new pattern of existence. "The development of creativity," he says, "becomes one of the most important conditions of our educational system. To teach toward creativity is to teach toward the future of society." Diversity, ingenuity, and individuality have made America great. Only these same qualities can keep her great.

INDIVIDUALIZED INSTRUCTION DEVELOPS ONE'S SELF-CONCEPT

Not only is the nature of individuality vital to the nation's welfare, but equally essential to the individual. Psychologists make the point that learning is an individual, a personal matter. It can most efficiently and effectively be accomplished if the individual's own unique cognitive style is recognized and accommodated.

There is no single theory of learning—there are many. Boys and girls do not learn in a single way nor to the same degree. They differ in how they learn, how much they learn, and how adept they are at using what they learn. To ignore the fact of different learning styles is both inefficient and wasteful both of teacher time and of student effort.

Nurturing individuality is particularly essential in developing the self-concept of the student. To develop ego strength, he must have practice in self-discovery, self-understanding, self-determination, and self-fulfillment. The student needs to assume increasing responsibility from an early age for decisions affecting his learning. This is a fault for which Edgar Friedenberg (12) condemns our schools and for which he attributes many of the problems which adolescents face. If one is to become a self-directed, self-actualized person, capable of functioning most efficiently in a democratic society, practice in directing his own actions is absolutely essential.

If a student's assignments are always handed to him so that he does not practice taking the responsibility of setting his own goals or does not learn to accept his own mistakes, the student grows to depend on others to make his decisions for him. This not only does irreparable damage to the individual's self-concept but makes him easy prey for those who would manipulate him.

Unfortunately, many pupils never discover what they can do for themselves because they have not had the opportunity to try. Followers, not self-directed individuals, result from autocratic situations. Plato once defined a slave as "the person who executes the wishes of another." When a teacher makes all the decisions and students are only passive recipients, slaves are the result—scholastic robots. Students need to pick and choose, to make choices (even some bad choices), but, above all, to gradually assume responsibility for their own learning. The concept of individuality decrees that boys and girls will vary as to how soon and to what degree they can handle responsibilities and make decisions connected with their educational program, but the time to begin "practice" is the day they begin formal schooling!

Despite the fact that we know motivation is higher when pupils are involved in planning, most educational programs are planned FOR, not BY, the students. There are books to read, papers to write, tests to take—all determined, in advance, by the teacher. After ten years of schooling we find high school juniors have almost nothing to say about what they study, where and how they will work on their lessons, or what materials they will use. It is absurd to think we can produce young men and women who are curious, creative, and self-fulfilling when they have been taught by school procedures only to be conforming.

SOME PRESENT PRACTICES

Most teachers and administrators will insist they are individualizing instruction. Unfortunately, when one gets into classrooms and carefully observes what is going on there, it is quite apparent that while educators generally support the individualization of instruction, in actuality, they are making little progress in that direction. For one thing, there are many definitions of the term. Frequently it is used to justify the activities currently found in the classroom. One could give many examples of classroom practices that are labeled "individualized instruction" by the teacher. Few focus on anything other than the acquisition of knowledge, however, and rarely is divergent thinking encouraged. Most teachers work exceedingly hard to wring out "correct" answers, and most classrooms are still very much instructor-dominated with "teacher talk" consuming from one-half to three-fourths of the time.

Flexible schedules, large group–small group instructional practices, multi-track plans, team teaching, continuous progress, nongrading, or similar manipulations of the time schedule or curriculum do not in themselves do much for the individual pupil. Adjustments of this type may appear spectacular on paper but they usually offer little more than token recognition of the gross, complex problems that pupil diversity presents. As John Goodlad (13) has pointed out, "No scheme of school or curriculum organization washes away human variability or the manifold problems of dealing with it instructionally. This, being so, much organizational effort clearly is misplaced."

Some schools have attempted to do more than adjust the organizational structure or curriculum. They have sought to recognize and make allowances for the great diversity in interests, competencies, drives, and other personal, social, and intellectual characteristics of students. However, while some progress has been made in recognizing pupil differences, not much has been accomplished in ministering to these differences other than in rate or speed of achievement. Little has been done to vary content, sequence, objectives, or paths to objectives. Even less consideration has been given to the self-concept of the learner, individual styles of learning, cultural influences on learning, or student responses to various styles of instruction.

Of course, schooling is conducted largely within the context of the social situation. Teachers, of necessity, must work a good deal of the time with groups of students, and the number of pupils per instructor seems to be increasing. Furthermore, materials and facilities to provide a well-stocked cafeteria for individual choices are frequently not available. Factors such as these mitigate against individual attention for pupils. Without genuine effort reflecting concern for individual differences and deliberate planning to encourage and provide for diversity, standardization is difficult to avoid. Grouping plans convenient to the teacher and the administration, inflexible curricula, standard texts and examinations all tend to squeeze students into common molds. This trend has led one prominent educator (14) to state that the typical student slogan of the day is, "I came, I saw, I concurred."

Educators must conscientiously avoid programs which accommodate the masses at the EXPENSE of individuals. Novel organizational patterns, realignment of pupils and teachers, and the use of mechanical devices should be undertaken with this fact clearly in mind. If it is in society's interest to provide educational experiences that enable individuals to flourish, and there seems to be general agreement that such is the case, then it is imperative that educators give top priority to what will be best for individuals when planning changes in the school program.

Recognizing and providing for individual differences, as imperative as these obligations may be, do not completely fulfill a school's responsibilities to its students. Educating the individual and nurturing individuality are not the same. A child's uniqueness is more than the total of all his individual differences.

DIRECTIONS FOR THE FUTURE

Individualization of instruction involves four vital dimensions. Provision must be made for each of the four if one is to say that a program is truly "individualized."

It is not enough simply to "diagnose" differences among students and to "prescribe" a variety of learning activities, as important as custom-tailored programs for individuals may be in their own right.

Nor is it enough to tinker with the school's curriculum or organizational pattern, although adjustments in both may be appropriate in any comprehensive plan to take care of individual differences.

Likewise, individualization is more than allowing students to make decisions and to assume responsibility for their own educational programs, despite the fact that democracy can only thrive where citizens have learned to be independent, self-directed, and responsible.

And, individualization of instruction is more than encouraging and nurturing uniqueness and creativity, although the very survival of our society may depend on pursuit of these qualities.

An individualized program that is worthy of that name must be characterized by more teacher awareness of differences among pupils and a greater array of alternative or learning activities. It will demonstrate that both curriculum and organizational patterns are flexible and subject to modification when pupil needs dictate it. Such a program will allow students to make decisions about what they study, when and how they study it, and involve the student in evaluating the effectiveness of his efforts, all activities designed to gradually place the responsibility for an educational program where it rightfully belongs ultimately—in the hands of the individual himself. And in a truly individualized program individuals will be encouraged to be different, to question, to dream, to create.

How can these kinds of things be accomplished in the classroom? The key is the TEACHER. It is his GOALS that make the difference. If the teacher's aim is to nurture diversity and uniqueness rather than standardization and alikeness, then the instructional procedures, the materials and activities, the degree of pupil participation in decisions about content, sequence, and learning activities will be toward that end.

Many teachers view themselves as the dispensers of knowledge and as the person "in charge" of the "educating" that goes on in the classroom. They find it very difficult, if not impossible, to view their role as one of producing the climate, providing the resources, stimulating the students to explore, investigate, and seek answers. In a rich, pregnant environment, the teacher's role becomes one of guiding and facilitating rather than directing.

Many teachers simply cannot accept such a role. Students, at an early age, can begin setting their own goals for learning. But the teacher determines whether they may. Students can plan productive learning activities, if the teacher recognizes this as an essential part of the learning experience. Students can learn to evaluate their own efforts, but the teacher may assume the role himself, thus encouraging students only to please him.

The extent and quality of individualization that takes place in a classroom is determined both by the teacher's definition of the term and the role he assigns himself in the classroom. Generally, across this land of ours teachers are setting the goals. Teachers are planning the activities. Teachers are determining alternatives and usually limiting, not expanding opportunities. Teachers are doing the evaluating. Teachers dominate the scene. That is why most schools are doing very little, except talk about individualization of instruction today. And yet, individuals and their variability comprise one of our most precious resources. It is absolutely imperative that instruction in our schools be "individualized" in the broadest sense of that term. How much longer can this nation allow its schools to ignore that fact?

References

1. HENRY, DAVID D., "Individual Competence and the National Welfare." *NASSP Bulletin*, Vol. 45, No. 264 (April 1961), 331–335.

2. Joint Project on the Individual and the School, *A Climate for Individuality*. Washington, D.C.: AASA, ASCD, NASSP, and NEA Department of Rural Education, 1965.

3. Rockefeller Panel Reports, *The Pursuit of Excellence: Education and the Future of America*. Garden City, N. Y.: Doubleday & Company, Inc., 1958.

4. FROMM, ERICH, *Escape from Freedom*. New York: Rinehart and Company, 1941.

5. RIESMAN, DAVID, *The Lonely Crowd*. Garden City, N. Y.: Doubleday & Company, Inc., 1953.

6. WHYTE, WILLIAM H., JR., *The Organization Man.* New York: Simon and Schuster, Inc., 1956.

7. FRIEDMAN, NORMAN, "The Schools and the Defeat of the Child," *This Magazine is About Schools.* Vol. One, Issue Two, August 1966.

8. TYLER, FRED T., AND WILLIAM A. BROWNELL, "Facts and Issues: A Concluding Statement." *Individualizing Instruction,* 61st Yearbook of the National Society for the Study of Education, Part 1. Chicago: University of Chicago Press, 1962.

9. ANDERSON, HAROLD H. (ED.), *Creativity and Its Cultivation.* (Addresses presented at the Interdisciplinary Symposia on Creativity, Michigan State University, 1957–58.) New York: Harper & Brothers, 1959.

10. ROGERS, CARL, *Creativity and Its Cultivation.* Harold H. Anderson (Ed.). New York: Harper & Brothers, 1959.

11. LOWENFELD, VICTOR, AND W. LAMBERT BRITTAIN, *Creative and Mental Growth.* New York: The Macmillan Company, 1964.

12. FRIEDENBERG, EDGAR Z., *The Vanishing Adolescent.* Boston: Beacon Press, 1959.

13. GOODLAD, JOHN I., *Planning and Organizing for Teaching.* Washington, D.C.: National Educational Association, 1963, p. 10.

14. BROWN, B. FRANK, quoted in "The Cost of Conformity," by Raymond Squires. *PTA Magazine,* Vol. 58, No. 7, March 1964.

QUEST FOR SELF

Ashley Montagu

In the western world the quest for self has for several millennia taken the form of an introverted aggrandizement of the self, a self-centeredness, in which the individual becomes the greater part of the whole and the remainder of the human world exists to minister to his needs.

Without doubt the worst offender in perpetuating this perverted version of the self is the Western Christian family, an organization for the training of its members in self-centeredness and the production of a high frequency of mental illness. By systematic training, the individual is inculcated with aspirations which end with self, the focus being upon his realizing himself in relation not to others but to the satisfaction of what his family and his culture tell him are his needs. It is not generally recognized that the Western Christian family—consisting of mother, father, and children, a self-contained unit, atomized and dissociated from other similar units—is an aberration, an abnormality. In other sections of the world people live together as members of extended families or families interrelated with other families, socially and by no means necessarily biologically. Emphasis is on the quality of human relationships rather than on the quantity one can learn to acquire of external validations of "success." *When a child is brought up in a socially interrelated group, he develops a self and a conscience which seek expression through the group and with involvement in the group.* When he socializes within a family

From *Childhood Education*, Vol. 41, No. 1 (September 1964), pp. 3–8. Reprinted by permission of Ashley Montagu and the Association for Childhood Education International, 3615 Wisconsin Avenue, N.W., Washington, D.C. Copyright © 1964 by the Association.

psychologically isolated from other families, in which parental attention is concentrated upon a rigorous condition of the child in what is expected of him by others and what he has a right in turn to expect from them, he emerges as an individualist regarding the rest of the world as his oyster.

INTERDEPENDENT FAMILIES

When children are brought up in a family within an interdependent group in which each is interdependent with each, in which mutualism rather than individualism and the competitiveness associated with it are the rule, they are likely to grow up as persons who consciously and rationally choose cooperation in place of competition and altruism in place of destructiveness. In the Western family, while the focus is on the individual and his growth in egocentricity, strong emotional ties are usually developed between parents and children in a far from healthy manner. Intensely developed constellations of emotions, which become repressed and remain unconscious, arise in relation to the parental figures. The child's incorporation of the imperatives of these parental figures tends toward the production of an overrigid conscience, together with repressed hatreds and anxieties which may later play havoc with such a person's ability to function in a healthy manner. Whatever their genetic potentials, the threads of the personality are woven upon the loom of the family; and in the creation of the self the family plays the fundamental role.

The quest for self as inculcated in the Western family structure is based on an erroneous conception of the idea of man, of what man is born as, and what man is born for. If we are ever to understand what man is born for, we had better begin re-examining some of our most strongly entrenched beliefs concerning the nature of man and what he is born as.

LOVE—IMPORTANT BASIC NEED

The doctrine of what our Victorian ancestors called "innate depravity" can no longer be seriously entertained. Man has an evolutionary history which renders it certain that the behavioral traits which have continuously been at the highest premium in his evolution—behaviorally as well as physically—have been intelligence, with a concomitant loss of instincts and the growth of cooperation and love. In the cultural evolution of man there has been a continuous feedback between genetic selection for these positive traits and behaviors which these traits have then rendered possible. All this has made possible increasing plasticity and educability and thus greater general adaptiveness to the cultural and physical environments.

Man is born with a highly organized system of basic needs—the need for oxygen, food, liquid, sleep, rest, activity, bowel and bladder elimination, and avoidance of noxious and dangerous stimuli. These are basic because they must be satisfied if the organism is to survive physically. We have learned, however, that for healthy mental functioning the most important of all needs is the need for love—not merely the need to be loved but the need also to love others. A definition of love is *behavior calculated to confer survival benefits in a creatively enlarging manner upon others*. In this conception of love we have an invaluable unifying principle which combines under one simple rubric the evolutionary facts, the facts of individual development, the facts of individual and social mental health. From whatever standpoint the principle of love is viewed, it turns out to have the highest adaptive value in the development of the group and the individual. The principle of love is a grand generalization like the principle of evolution itself, which not only serves to explain and bring together a great disparity of apparently unrelated phenomena but also serves as a touchstone for the development and conduct of human beings. *The best definition of mental health that I know is the ability to love.* Insofar as anyone falls short of that ability, to that extent he is crippled in his capacity to relate himself in the most important of all ways toward others; that is, the ability to stimulate his potentialities in such a way that they develop harmoniously and to the optimum.

EDUCATION IN HUMAN RELATIONS

Mental health may be defined as the ability to love and the ability to work. Those of us in education should direct our activities toward helping individuals achieve mental health. Educational institutions should be reassessed and reorganized toward that end through knowledge now available, which tells us not only what human beings are born as but also what they are born for: *to realize their intrinsic nature and to fulfill themselves.* The educator's function is to enable the individual successfully to negotiate the journey in search of self by giving him sustenances and stimulation to pursue that journey as creatively as possible. This requires teachers who are themselves able to love—for *it is by being loved that one learns to love,* just as one learns to speak by being spoken to. Those teachers will not only communicate the meaning of love to their pupils, but it will be their task also to communicate through their own example the facts and theory upon which education in human relations is based; in other words, the science—that is to say the theory, the art, and the practice—of human relations.

If we are told, "But that should be the job of the parents," the answer is, "Of course it should, but who is to create parents capable of doing what they ought if their own parents have not been taught how to do so?" In such cases the teacher must stand *in loco parentis* and always in proximate relation to the parental role, for he will always need to amplify and correct the work of the parents. That is principally what a teacher's function should be. And if the teacher asks, "Am I to take over the parents' job when the parents have failed to do what they ought?" the answer is, "Without question and in bounden duty." *The one thing the developing human being must not be failed in is the sustenance and support he expects and has a right to inherit.*

SELF-GROWTH RELATED TO OTHERS

In his individual behavioral development the human organism repeats the development of the species. From the symbiotic relation with the mother in the womb to the continuing symbiosis after it is born, the human organism unequivocally and clearly exhibits a directiveness in its behavioral growth and development in which *growth and development of the self proceed together with increasing growth and development in interdependence, in relation always with others.* The directiveness of the organism is toward growth and development in the realization of its need for relatedness. All its needs are so structured as to require stimulations enabling the organism to realize its capacities for relatedness and turn those capacities into acted-out abilities. The self grows in relatedness and develops by what it feeds on. No one is born with a self, though all are born with genetic potentialities for realization of a self which are never alike in any two individuals, with the possible exception of identical twins. Allowing for genetic differences, those genetic potentialities will enable the individual to develop a self only as he is exposed to appropriate environmental stimuli.

CREATING OWN SELF

The organism is oriented in the direction of self-creation; but evidence all about us shows that we rarely permit human beings to create themselves, that instead we impose a self

Copyright © 2022 by Craig Henderson

All rights reserved. No part of this book may be reproduced in any form or by any electronic or mechanical means, including information storage and retrieval systems, without permission in writing from the publisher, except by a reviewer, who may quote brief passages in a review. Scanning, uploading, and electronic distribution of this book or the facilitation of such without the permission of the publisher is prohibited. Please purchase only authorized electronic editions, and do not participate in or encourage electronic piracy of copyrighted materials. Your support of the author's rights is appreciated. Any member of educational institutions wishing to photocopy part or all of the work for classroom use, or anthology, should send inquiries to Grove Atlantic, 154 West 14th Street, New York, NY 10011 or permissions@groveatlantic.com.

FIRST EDITION

Published simultaneously in Canada
Printed in the United States of America

First Grove Atlantic hardcover edition: November 2022

This book is set in 11.5-pt. Scala Pro
by Alpha Design & Composition of Pittsfield, NH.

Library of Congress Cataloging-in-Publication data is available for this title.

ISBN 978-0-8021-5970-0
eISBN 978-0-8021-5971-7

Atlantic Monthly Press
an imprint of Grove Atlantic
154 West 14th Street
New York, NY 10011

Distributed by Publishers Group West

groveatlantic.com

22 23 24 25   10 9 8 7 6 5 4 3 2 1

upon them. We teach children to follow within predestinate grooves etched out upon them by their socializers. Intrinsic conditionings become "second nature." In this process of socialization, intrinsic nature is lost. This is the great tragedy that befalls many human beings. The real evil lies in the difference between what a human being is capable of becoming and what in fact he has been caused to become.

Selves are not born but made and they are made according to the pattern prevailing in the culture or particular segments thereof. In our culture we do not form selves by providing selves with the skills and tools designed to enable them to continue to make themselves—as a sculptor works upon his material to produce the finished sculpture. What we do is attempt to make selves that will conform to a common mold. We produce stereotyped minds that go through life repeating clichés and stereotypes under the impression that this is what one means by "thinking." *We produce unquestioning minds in frightening numbers, minds unable to evaluate evidence critically for themselves.*

NOT RITUAL BUT ACTION

In training children in rote repetition and regurgitation of "facts," we deceive them into believing this is learning and what they have learned in this way is both knowledge and wisdom. Such teaching is the antithesis of what teaching should be. *Learning is the continuous adventure of thinking analytically, critically, and independently for oneself, continually questioning basic principles* and what is taken for granted or held axiomatic. We teach children hypocrisy by ritual lying and group incantation and forget that knowledge, learning, courage, and love are the four great chords of might; we forget that what is implied by these words means not so much what we have been prepared to get from the group as what we each can do for the group's betterment. "One nation indivisible, under God, with liberty and justice for all" is a fine ideal but abrogated if one fails to teach the lesson that fine words are but ritual incantations unless followed by action, that the meaning of a word is the action it produces. The natural purpose of words is to put and keep human beings in touch with one another and not to divide them by setting up ideals which satisfy the need for ritual.

TEACHERS NEED TO VALUE THEMSELVES

In a critical position in relation to the whole of humanity, the teacher in our culture has a tremendous responsibility. The most important members of the community, *teachers are the unacknowledged legislators of the world.* It is time they began valuing themselves at their real worth, for no one will begin to esteem teachers at their true worth until teachers value themselves and their work highly.

In the quest for self, teachers have a job of work to do on themselves before they begin working on others. They must begin the task of working on themselves in the desired direction—in the ability to love.

THREE R'S AND HUMAN RELATIONS

The human infant is born the most immature and most dependent and interdependent creature on earth, who must learn everything he comes to learn and do from other human beings. Human beings are born without instincts. Unlike other animals they have to learn how to *respond* and not react to their environment, although some of our educational institutions teach them how to react but not how to respond. In other words, I regard our educational institutions as organizations designed to replace in human beings the instinctual mechanisms by which other animals react to their environment. A human being should be taught to think twice and thrice, to respond and never to react. And we, realizing the dependency of the newborn infant, the child, upon others, must not fail him but give him all the stimulations and supports required for the development of his potentialities, for being what it is possible for him to be—one who can relate himself creatively, cooperatively, and harmoniously toward others. We need to recognize that the three R's can never be anything more than skills, techniques which are quite secondary to their main purpose—the maximum realization of whatever potentials the individual is endowed with, of self-fulfillment. *Our educational institutions should be institutions for the teaching of the theory, the science, the practice; that is, the art of human relations first and reading, writing, and arithmetic second.*

In the quest for self, teachers have first to prepare themselves for the work they will be required to perform in this connection, because the greatest gift a teacher has to offer to his children is his own personality; and when everything else is forgotten what will be left will be the personality—that is, the meaning—of the teacher. It is not the subject matter, the content, that is the message; it is the method by which one teaches—one's personality. Perfection in this ability to love is almost never attained by anyone. But the one who makes this effort toward perfection goes a long way in the right direction.

THWARTING CAUSES AGGRESSIVE BEHAVIOR

It is the moral obligation of every teacher to acquaint himself with the best that has been said, thought, and done on the subject of man's intrinsic nature and the quest for self. In this connection the doctrine of innate depravity, which we inherited from St. Paul—perhaps the first intellectual of the Western world—the doctrine of original sin, and the doctrine of the "orneriness" of human nature, that human beings are born ornery, naughty, evil in the flesh, is unsound. The wars, the rapine, the warfare, the inhumanity of man toward man, the juvenile delinquency have served to confirm St. Paul's view that man is an ornery, nasty, evil, maniacal, selfish, hostile, aggressive brat. *Human beings are not naturally or innately any of these things—they learn to be all these things. They are not born this way.* The most ornery creature—the most hostile, the most aggressive, the biggest troublemaker, and the biggest problem child—is the child who is being most failed in his need for love; he is responding in this rebellious way because he wishes to draw attention to his need for love and wishes to compel the attention to his need for love from those who may yet be capable of giving it to him. So-called "aggressive" behavior in a child (or anyone else) is simply love frustrated. A frustration is the thwarting of an expected satisfaction. A child's thwarted need for love will compel him to struggle as if for air. If it is withheld from him, he may indulge in violent behavior in order to procure that air or the food he needs. The most important of all the foods for the development of his personality is love. Any child who does not acquire a sufficient amount of it is truly among the disinherited. It is not the most lovable child or person who is most in need of love but the most unlovable.

TEACHERS SHOULD REASSESS VALUES

Everything I have said has not been so much an opinion as a datum of experience which can be verified. This is what the scientist is interested in. He is not interested in proving anything to be one way or another or in collecting facts or in a willingness to believe or disbelieve. He is interested in one thing and that is in what is and, having stated it, will hope that it will be checked and verified by others; this is what you ought to do, remembering in the words of Lord Acton, the great Catholic English historian, that *liberty is not the power of doing what we like but the right of being able to do what we ought.* The effort necessary to acquire this information can be just as enjoyable as teaching. One of the purposes of education is to make work enjoyable.

Since the school is one of the principal agencies in the transmission of the culture's values to the child, it is of equally great importance that teachers should reassess values they are called upon to inculcate into their children. The abstract inconsideration of good intentions is not enough. To be a teacher is to be responsible and not to be the mere echo of other voices. Nor is there any point in making recurrent unmeaning genuflections in the direction of what one thinks ought to be, without making the concomitant effort to convert what ought to be into what is. The teacher's task is not an end in itself, but a means of communicating humanity, to join loving-kindness to learning, and setting oneself in order as the basis for the practice of good human relations. It is personal influence which determines the size of a life; and *in the quest for self it is the teacher's personal influence that will count* as much as and in a large number of cases more than anyone else's *in helping the individual realize and fulfill himself.*

The present condition of Western man is not irremediable, but a culture which produces ineffectual human beings is badly in need of revaluation. The teachers of the land must carry out that revaluation and the changes it dictates. They are the best qualified, or should be, to remedy the ills to which man is subjected so that he may learn to live in dignity and enjoy the autonomy and power of his own personality, of his own self.

FOSTERING
SELF-DIRECTION

Arthur W. Combs

Schools which do not produce self-directed citizens have failed everyone—the student, the profession, and the society they are designed to serve. The goals of modern education cannot be achieved without self-direction. We have created a world in which there is no longer a common body of information which everyone must have. The information explosion has blasted for all time the notion that we can feed all students the same diet. Instead, we have to adopt a cafeteria principle in which we help each student select what he most needs to fulfill his potentialities. This calls for student cooperation and acceptance of major responsibility for his own learning.

As Earl Kelley has suggested, the goal of education in the modern world must be the production of increasing uniqueness. This cannot be achieved in autocratic atmospheres where all decisions are made by the teachers and administration while students are reduced to passive followers of the established patterns. Authoritarian schools are as out of date in the world we live in as the horse and buggy. Such schools cannot hope to achieve our purposes. Worse yet, their existence will almost certainly defeat us.

From *Educational Leadership*, Vol. 23, No. 5 (February 1966), pp. 373–76. Reprinted with permission of the Association for Supervision and Curriculum Development and Arthur W. Combs. Copyright © 1966 by the Association.

The world we live in demands self-starting, self-directing citizens capable of independent action. The world is changing so fast we cannot hope to teach each person what he will need to know in twenty years. Our only hope to meet the demands of the future is the production of intelligent, independent people. Even our military establishment, historically the most authoritarian of all, has long since discovered that fact. For twenty years the armed forces have been steadily increasing the degree of responsibility and initiative expected of even the lowest echelons. The modern war machine cannot be run by automatons. It must be run by *thinking* men.

Much of the curriculum of our current schools is predicated on a concept of learning conceived as the acquisition of right answers and many of our practices mirror this belief. Almost anyone can pick them out. Here are a few which occur to me:

Preoccupation with right answers; insistence upon conformity; cookbook approaches to learning; overconcern for rules and regulations; preoccupation with materials and things instead of people; the solitary approach to learning; the delusion that mistakes are sinful; emphasis on memory rather than learning; emphasis on grades rather than understanding and content details rather than principles.

Meanwhile, psychologists are telling us that learning is a *personal* matter; individual and unique. It is not controlled by the teacher. It can only be accomplished with the cooperation and involvement of the student in the process. Providing students with information is not enough. People rarely misbehave because they do not know any better. The effectiveness of learning must be measured in behavior change: whether students *behave differently* as a consequence of their learning experience. This requires active participation by the student. So learning itself is dependent upon the capacity for self-direction.

TOWARD SELF-DIRECTION

What is needed of us? How can we produce students who are more self-directed?

1. We Need to Believe This Is Important.   If we do not think self-direction is important, this will not get done. People are too pressed these days to pay much attention to things that are not important. Everyone does what seems to him to be crucial and urgent. It seems self-evident that independence and self-direction are necessary for our kind of world. Why then has self-direction been given such inadequate attention? It is strange we should have to convince ourselves of its importance.

Unfortunately, because a matter is self-evident is no guarantee that people will really put it into practice. It must somehow be brought into clear figure in the forefront of our striving if it is to affect behavior. Everyone knows it is important to vote, too, yet millions regularly fail to vote. To be effective as an objective, each of us must hold the goal of self-direction clear in our thinking and high in our values whenever we are engaged in planning or teaching of any kind.

This is often not easy to do because self-direction is one of those goals which *everyone* is supposed to be working for. As a result, almost no one regards it as urgent! For each person, his own special duties are so much clearer, so much more pressing and his derelictions so much more glaring if he fails to produce. The goals we hold in common do not redound so immediately to our credit or discredit. They are therefore set aside while we devote our energies to the things that *really* matter to us.

To begin doing something about self-direction we must, therefore, begin by declaring its importance, not as a lofty sentiment but as an absolute essential. It must be given a place of greater concern than subject matter itself, for a very simple reason: It is far more important than subject matter. Without self-direction no content matters much. It is not enough that it be published in the handbook as a "Goal of Education." Each of us at every level must ask himself: Do I really think self-direction is important and what am I doing about it?

2. Trust in the Human Organism. Many of us grew up in a tradition which conceived of man as basically evil and certain to revert to bestial ways if someone did not control him. Modern psychologists tell us this view is no longer tenable. From everything we can observe in humans and animals the basic striving of the organism is inexorably toward health both physical and mental. It is this growth principle on which doctors and psychotherapists depend to make the person well again. If an organism is free to do so—it can, will, it *must* move in positive ways. The organism is not our enemy. It wants the same things we do, the achievement of adequacy. Yet alas, how few believe this and how timid we are to trust our students with self-direction.

A recent best selling book, *Summerhill*, by A. S. Neill has fascinated many educators. In it Neill describes the absolute trust he placed in the children under his care. Many teachers are shocked by his unorthodox procedures and the extreme behavior of some of the children. But whether one approves of Neill's school or not, the thing which impressed me most was this: Here was a man who dared to trust children far beyond what most of us would be willing to risk. Yet, all the things we are so afraid might happen if we did give them such freedom, never happened! For forty years the school continued to turn out happy, effective citizens as well as, or better than, its competitors. It is time we give up fearing the human organism and learn to trust and use its built-in drives toward self-fulfillment. After all, the organism has had to be pretty tough to survive what we have done to it through the ages.

Responsibility and self-direction are learned. They must be acquired from experiences, from being given opportunities to be self-directing and responsible. You cannot learn to be self-directing if no one permits you to try. Human capacities are strengthened by use but atrophy with disuse. If young people are going to learn self-direction, then it must be through being *given* many opportunities to exercise such self-direction throughout the years they are in school. Someone has observed that our schools are operated on a directly contrary principle. Children are allowed more freedom of choice and self-direction in kindergarten (when they are presumably least able to handle it) and each year thereafter are given less and less, until, by the time they reach college, they are permitted practically no choice at all! This overdraws the case, to be sure, but there is enough truth in the statement to make one uncomfortable. If we are to produce independent, self-starting people we must do a great deal more to produce the kinds of experiences which will lead to these ends.

3. The Experimental Attitude.   If we are going to provide young people with increased opportunity for self-direction, we must do it with our eyes open *expecting* them to make mistakes. This is not easy, for the importance of "being right" is in our blood. Education is built on right answers. Wrong ones are regarded as failures to be avoided like the plague. Unfortunately, such attitudes stand squarely in the way of progress toward self-direction and independence.

People too fearful of mistakes cannot risk trying. Without trying, self-direction, creativity, and independence cannot be discovered. To be so afraid of mistakes that we kill the desire to try is a tragedy. Autonomy, independence, and creativity are the products of being willing to look and eager to try. If we discourage these elements we do so at our peril. In the world we live in, victory is reserved only for the courageous and inventive. It is possible we may lose the game by making mistakes. We will not even get in the game if we are afraid to try.

Experimentation and innovation must be encouraged everywhere in our schools, in teachers as well as students. Each of us needs to be engaged in a continuous process of trying something new. The kind of experimentation which will make the difference to education in the long run is not that produced by the professional researcher with the aid of giant computers but by the everyday changes in goals and processes brought about by the individual teacher in the classroom.

To achieve this, teachers need to be freed of pressures and details by the administration for the exercise of self-direction and creativity. In addition, each of us must accept the challenge and set about a systematic search for the barriers we place in the path of self-direction for ourselves, our colleagues, and our students. This should suggest all kinds of places for experimentation where we can begin the encouragement of self-direction. One of the nice things about self-direction is that it does not have to be taught. It only needs to be encouraged and set free to operate.

4. The Provision of Opportunity. The basic principle is clear. To produce more self-directed people it is necessary to give more opportunity to practice self-direction. This means some of us must be willing to give up our traditional prerogatives to make all the decisions. Education must be seen, not as providing right answers but as confrontation with problems; not imaginary play problems either, but *real* ones in which decisions count.

Experiences calling for decision, independence, and self-direction must be the daily diet of children, including such little decisions as what kinds of headings and margins a paper should have and big ones like the courses to be taken next year. They must also include decisions about goals, techniques, time, people, money, meals, rules, and subject matter.

If we are to achieve the objective of greater self-direction, I see no alternative to the fuller acceptance of students into partnership in the educative endeavor. Our modern goal for education, "the optimal development of the individual," cannot be achieved without this. Such an aim requires participation of the student and his wholehearted cooperation in the process. This is not likely to be accomplished unless students have the feeling they matter and their decisions count. Few of us are deeply committed to tasks imposed upon us; and students are not much different. Self-direction is learned from experience. What better, more meaningful experience could be provided than participation in the decisions about one's own life and learning?

The basic belief of democracy is that when people are free they can find their own best ways. Though all of us profess our acceptance of this credo, it is distressing how few of us dare to put it to work. Whatever limits the capacity of our young people to accept both the challenge and the responsibilities of that belief is destructive to all of us. It is time we put this belief to work and to expression in the education of our young as though we really meant it.

EDUCATIONAL CONDITIONS ESSENTIAL TO GROWTH IN INDIVIDUALITY

Fred T. Wilhelms

Even a casual student of the world's history must see that men have grown to greater stature in some times and places than in others. And not merely in physical size and strength; for, though the physical differences have been striking enough, they have been dwarfed by vast ranges in power of spirit.

Physical prowess was the least part of the force when the Hellenic few beat off the Persian horde. Something far beyond strength of body produced the bustling energy of the Italian Renaissance, the surging confidence of Elizabethan England, and the incredible sages of the American frontier. Every society offers a curriculum of life, which teaches men to be men, or reduces most of them to a whimpering mass.

What has enabled some societies to produce so much individual vigor? The answer probably lies in certain conditions of the social climate. Similarly within the schools, to release the powers latent in each individual, our primary effort must be to establish a climate favorable to growth. Fortunately, in the smaller society of the school, we can in some measure plan the child's environment; our professional staffs can give technical expression to insights gained by experience and research not only in education but also in psychology and re-

Reprinted from *NASSP Bulletin*, Vol. 48 (Jan. 1964), pp. 92–103, by permission of Fred T. Wilhelms and the National Association of Secondary School Principals.

lated disciplines. We had better be modest in all this, for certainly we cannot claim to know all we need to know about the optimal "growing" of human beings. But even now we can confidently describe a few basic conditions which are essential and which, taken together, will assure high power-development.

STIMULATION

There is increasing evidence that intelligence itself is in considerable degree an environmental artifact. Perhaps, instead of speaking of a child's intelligence, we ought to condition ourselves to think of his "developed intelligence." There may be some yet undefined "ceiling" to each child's intellectual powers; but it is a safe estimate that few ever reach it, and that many live out their lives shockingly far below it. It appears that those who rise nearest to it are the ones who have had opportunity and encouragement to respond to a tremendous wealth and variety of stimuli.

It looks as if there is a very great premium on *early* stimulation, in the first months and years of a child's life. Later richness of stimulation may be hard put to repair an early lack. Therefore the child's family must bear a heavy responsibility in this area. Furthermore, only the home and community can turn out-of-school hours into a time of great and diverse opportunity to respond.

Nevertheless, the school and classroom can be blankly barren or vividly stimulating. The very texture and appearance of building and hall and room can invite exploration and adventure. So modest a matter as how charmingly and invitingly books are put in reach can make a great difference in how a child will venture into the worlds of thought and phantasy. There are rooms where living nature is brought in, to be touched and fondled and wondered at. There are ingenious teachers who get their children amazing opportunities to "fool around" in unconscious creativity with the beginnings of diverse arts and crafts and the tools of technology and science. There are schools that open up the community to a new level of seeing—its museums and galleries and cultural resources, but also its workaday operations in the very business of life. Above all, there are teachers who by their whole manner and temperament, as well as by technique, subtly encourage children to respond vividly, to take risks, to toy with ideas, to open themselves up to stimuli. In several cities programs of various sorts, including some popularly called "Higher Horizons," have achieved striking results by opening up the range and quality of stimulation.

Lest it be thought that all this portends the development of the young person at the expense of subject matter, let us hasten to add that well-taught subject matter is the school's chief instrument for stimulation. Just as a man strolling through woods or mountains has more to respond to if he knows something of botany and geology, so a child's whole environment grows richer in stimuli as he learns to read, to work with line and color, to comprehend a map and be aware of history, and so on and on. Literature, the social studies, mathematics, the sciences—every worthwhile subject has new worlds to open to speculation and response.

In fact, in this connection, we might almost set separately another "condition for self-actualization": the sort of condition that helps each youngster develop a feeling for learning for its own intrinsic value. Certainly we also want him to see the "instrumental" value of learning—that it provides him the tools he needs. But there is something which transcends this.

A child can learn to take deep and increasing joy in the very process of learning. There can come to be a pleasurable tension in the hard challenge to stretch his thought, an exultation in the problem solved. Described thus, the thing may sound frothy, like mere intellectual play. But little by little there can be built in an increasing element of discipline. And this very disciplinedness—the conscious power to stick at a tough problem till it is mastered—can in its turn be a great source of self-enjoyment. This writer recalls from his high school years vivid hours of struggle with geometry "originals" deliberately sought out by a small group from advanced college texts. And even the strain of producing this paper has had a half-hidden undercurrent of the joy of battle. Youngsters, with their ebullient energies, can learn to take to learning with spontaneous delight.

The examples above have all been pitched to *intellectual* growth through stimulation. Probably they could have been made equally well with respect to growth in human relations, leadership, or other dimensions.

There is a legitimate concern about the feverish overstimulation of some children. But one suspects the problem is one of adult pressures and emotional forcing. A child at his first circus may eat too much popcorn and drink too much pink lemonade for his stomach's good. But one need not fear that any child left free to use his eyes will crack his skull with what he takes in.

RESPONSIBLE FREEDOM

History will support a rough generalization: that an increase in human freedom will generate a rise in human productivity —whether productivity is measured in terms of ideas and the arts or in terms of economic goods and services. A chart of the productivity of American immigrants before and after they came to these freer shores would make the point.

For children, too, freedom is a tremendous stimulant. One need not leap to the position that freedom must be total, immediately or ever, or that guidance and the setting of limits are not essential. But the very nature of growth demands a steady increase in command of one's own life space. Regimentation is dulling. It can produce only efficiency, if that.

Freedom—especially, perhaps, when it is *growing*—is exhilarating. It leads to exploring, to the release of the creative impulse, trying oneself out with daring, to attempting what is more difficult than what one has previously achieved. All this is essential to a young person's stretching himself, finding his powers, and getting confidence in them.

Of course, because schools deal with groups, freedom must be within a context of a certain orderliness. This is perfectly possible—and consonant with the demands of life in a society. But teachers and administrators may unconsciously purchase orderliness and quick efficiency at the price of essential freedom. If they do, the development of each individual will be by so much the less complete.

An essential ingredient of freedom is *responsibility*. Without it freedom is meaningless. And responsibility is *not* the negative side of the coin of freedom. We betray a misconception of the human organism when we call responsibility the cost one pays for freedom; when half-punitively, having yielded some freedom to a child, we threaten him with, "But you'll have to take the responsibility if your choice goes wrong."

Responsibility is a good in itself. The growing human organism—perhaps especially at adolescence—intuitively yearns for it. In truth, our society may be short-changing its young people more by denial of responsibility than by crimping of liberty. For growing responsibility is essential to self-testing, to a developing sense of capacity, to a toughening of inner fiber. A person rises to full stature only as the demands upon him challenge him to rise. And without responsibility, growth can never be complete.

Nevertheless, responsibility can be harsh and frightening. Loadings of responsibility impossibly beyond a child's developed capacity can be frustrating and can lead to defeat and withdrawal. The artistry of home and school lies in creating conditions for full stretch without introducing the pressures that distort.

SUPPORT

Stimulation and freedom and responsibility introduce risk-taking, with the chance of failure. The whole thing is frustrated if the child will not take the opportunities with their attendant risks. He will take them only if he can afford to. And he can afford to only if he lives in an environment of support.

This does not mean that the child is to be protected from the real consequences of his choices—that, after all, he is to have freedom without responsibility—though it does mean he must be protected from making choices whose possible consequences may be disastrous beyond what he can bear. What it does demand is that for him *as a person* it can be all right to fail; that while he is suffering the consequences of an error he does not also have to suffer the loss of positive regard from those who matter most to him.

The highest form of support is love, unconditional love. There is unquestionable scientific evidence—added recently to the long perceptions of religion, philosophy, and the arts —that love is the prime condition of growth. The unloved person atrophies, and may in desperation make bizarre and self-defeating attempts to gain human status. The person securely rooted from infancy in unshakable love has strengths which almost nothing else can destroy. As Brock Chisholm has written, "The time has gone when psychologists and psychiatrists are shy about using the word love. It is known now that love is a physical and biological need of the child; if he gets it, his development is facilitated and if he does not get it his development is going to be slower and more difficult." [1]

But, at its ultimate level, love is the primary obligation of home and family. Probably the school cannot and should not obligate itself to supply love in this same deep sense. We may

[1] Brock Chisholm, "On Education: A Challenge for Educators," 1954 Asilomar Conference of the Mental Health Society of Northern California.

only drive excellent teachers to a falsely guilty despair by the excessive demand that they must love every child—if "love" in this context is taken to mean the same thing as what a mother feels for her child. A solid commitment to the ideal expressed by "acceptance" will be far better than sentimental, wishy-washy verbalisms about "love." For the mental health of our best teachers, as well as for the definition of our task, we greatly need to define what the supporting role of the school really is.

Certainly that role is no small one. A school can be unflinchingly loyal to a child when he is in trouble—even if he brought the trouble down on his own head and even if the school has to take stern disciplinary action. Knowing that human behavior is always caused, a teacher can be expected to be *understanding*, even if he cannot understand each child's every action—and even if he has to see to it that some actions stop. A school can maneuver against children's cruelties amongst themselves—the isolation of some unfortunates, the picking on a few. It can help greatly to have each child seen by his peers and by himself as a person worthy of his place.

Whatever the method, the necessity is inexorable. If a child is to grow to his full individuality, he *must* be living in an environment where he feels himself to belong, where he is wanted and respected and dignified. He *must* have the support identified by Rogers as "unconditional positive regard." If we school people cannot commit ourselves to love, in the parental sense, we *can* commit ourselves to a kindly warmth and acceptance and a climate of sunny affection. Or, if we cannot do even that, we must face frankly the inevitable losses, for of all conditions of full humane growth that which is akin to love is undoubtedly the foremost.

SUCCESS

Visualize for a moment the effect of support and success upon a baby born into a good and loving home. In his helpless time he depends on others for everything. His mother feeds him when he is hungry, handling him lovingly as she does so. His diapers are changed when they become uncomfortable. He is bathed to the accompaniment of fun and affection. When he signals distress there is solicitude to relieve it. Increasingly the whole family, and friends, play with him, pet him, adore him. Unwavering love lays foundations of what Erikson calls *basic trust.* "It's a pretty good world, and people like me."

In a little while he is not so helpless. He begins reaching out for things to do. His family encourage him; with imagination, they keep supplying him new things to master. He bangs his rattle and they chuckle affectionately. He grabs a spoon wrong side up and even when he smears his face with food they lead him on to learn. They gather 'round to applaud his first steps. There are failures, too; he bumps his little bottom many a time in a way that makes adults wince. But the little successes mount up, and his image of himself rises with them. "I'm a guy who can do things—more things all the time."

Then it comes time for the school to carry on. Will it continue imaginatively to bring before him new challenges just within his powers? Will it continue the kindly affection when he falls down? Will it lead him on to new successes, dramatizing each one to him a little bit? Will it provide an atmosphere in which he can make positive gains from his inevitable and necessary failures?

Or, for him, being what he is, will school be a place where he learns he is a failure?

The difference will be crucial. The long, balanced build-up of success upon success—each releasing energy for the next, bigger try—is essential to a self-concept that permits full growth. It is a just criterion of a school whether every student can go home most days with the taste of success on his tongue, or whether some shall be foredoomed to a steady diet of failure. The criterion is a harsh one, for it is no easy thing to make success steadily possible for youngsters of enormously differing abilities. One can only repeat that somehow it has to be done. It may help to define the concept more precisely.

First, the success experience must be authentic, not faked. A "no failure" policy of grading and promotion may be justified on other grounds, but it cannot create success by fiat.

Second, the inward need for successes does not imply that there shall be no failures. Quite the contrary; a child who is stimulated and supported to press out to the edge of his abilities will "fail" often—far more often than the child who has not been encouraged to be bold. And, properly handled, the failures will be good for him, helping him to a realistic image of himself and the world. But there is a vast difference between *having some failures* out at the edges, and *being a failure* down the middle of one's life stream. The latter is corrosive and will even dry up the energy required to keep trying. It is plain social immorality to force a child to be in school or in some class and then load the situation in such a way that he—being what he is, *for whatever reason*—must inevitably be a failure.

Third, success need not mean being "the best." It merely means doing well what one needs to do—and knowing that one has done it. In school terms, it means learning what one needs to learn, making a genuine contribution to oneself and to the group.

Schools need to provide a great diversity of *ways to succeed*. A good model for them will be the American society at large, for it lays before men and women many, many ways to succeed. These ways may not all seem equally lofty or important. But for each person his way to success is authentic. The truck driver need not change himself into a scientist to succeed. A good farmer or a good housewife is as genuine as a good lawyer or a good author. There are many ways to achieve.

Schools can do far more than they have done to provide a similar diversity of *ways to succeed*, and give each one dignity. Although good teachers intuitively do some of it constantly, schools remain far narrower than the general society in the range of goodness they accept. When curriculum is being planned every unit of work should be tested to see how many roads to success are built into it—how many ways for individuals to contribute diversely to the common whole. The entire school environment can be examined for opportunities to help each child work and learn in his private way. The main prerequisite is simply the recognition that in school—as in society—it is all right to come at things in different ways and even to arrive at different destinations.

COMMITMENT

The genie in his bottle—with his vast energies in turmoil, stoppered up—was no more helpless than the person who cannot commit himself.

The pattern is all too common: The man or woman who cannot love, because to love means entrusting oneself unreservedly to another. The youth who "plays it cool," keeping himself a little detached, unable to plunge wholeheartedly into any cause; he is not merely "cool"—he is *frozen* within himself.

No one can grow to his full stature until he can come into full and free communication with the people and the world about him, until he can invest his full energy into something outside himself, taking all the risks of rebuff and failure.

Schools can help enormously. A deft teacher can encourage individuals and groups toward idealistic ventures that have a high chance of success, sympathetically cushioning the occasional fall and putting it into perspective. When, in San Francisco, the jacket-gang boys enlisted in "Youth for Service" went out on Saturdays to help the needy, they learned a new way of investing something more than their restless energies. They learned what it feels like to throw oneself in. In a thousand smaller ways, schools can help to build the pattern. There is some power in a boy or girl that can be realized only by spending it.

SELF-INSIGHT

If, for a given child, the foregoing conditions have been met, he will already have had great opportunity to learn about himself. Under stimulation and with the encouragement of past success, he will have explored widely and he will have tried himself out in a multitude of ways. With the support of love and loyalty and understanding, he will have had the assurance to look at himself and all around him with a clear eye. He will have had little inward need to clamp down his perceptions, to distort the messages that come to him.

Yet the matter of understanding and accepting oneself appears to be so basic that even in the happiest cases the school may well go even further. Furthermore, only some children will have learned so happy a lesson; many will only have learned to mistrust themselves and others, to deprecate their own potential. Very likely they will have built up defenses and learned to distort their perceptions. The situation is very serious. One of every ten children sitting before us seems destined to move one day into a mental hospital. Many more than that suffer the cruel torments of guilt and conflict. Virtually all are tied down below their full potential by the miseries of self-doubt. Adolescence, with its bewildering changes, brings all the strains to crescendo.

What does all this mean? Shall the teacher turn psychiatrist and labor at a dilute form of psychoanalysis or therapy? No. There would be grave danger in that. But everyday subject matter can be turned to great advantage. For example, the work of Ojemann [2] at the State University of Iowa has begun

[2] Ralph H. Ojemann, Eugene E. Levitt, William H. Lyle, Jr., and Maxine F. Whiteside, "The Effects of a 'Causal' Teacher-Training Program and Certain Curricular Changes on Grade School Children," *Journal of Experimental Education*, 24:95–115, December 1955.

to show that teachers who understand the causation of human behavior can use ordinary subjects and school-like experiences to deepen children's understanding. In the process, it has been shown, children's blinding prejudices and needs for quick certainty decreases.

Certainly, if we choose, we can use the natural sciences to teach young people much about themselves. The study of literature is almost meaningless if it is not used to deepen understanding of self and of the general human condition. There is no reason why we should not incorporate into the social studies *much* more than we have of what is being brought to light about people, in psychology, social psychology, cultural anthropology, sociology, and economics. Philosophy itself is not so impossible a thing to employ with children and youth as common school practice would make it seem. The very reason of existence of such disciplines is the solving of human problems. No one who comprehends their true function will see a threat of dilution of their content or of loss of intellectual vigor when they are *used for people.*

If we mean to help each individual to the full assumption of his powers we must help him to a calmer comfortableness with himself. There is abundant evidence that with self-insight comes increasing self-acceptance. It does not mean the end of attempts to improve; it reveals the proper targets for self-improvement and releases energy for the life-long task.

And with self-insight and self-acceptance, the evidence shows, comes understanding and acceptance of others. Once we have faced the best and the worst within ourselves, we can appreciate the best and sympathize with the worst in others. We can move into free and open communication with our fellows. We can take the world as it is, strive to improve it, and as mature persons live with what must be lived with.

SUMMARY

What we have tried to say thus far is that, to foster individuality, the most fundamental thing is to secure for each child a wholesome climate for growth. We believe that the minimum essentials of such a climate are rich stimulation and stretch, responsible freedom growing with the years, the support of love and acceptance, a balanced pattern of success experiences, encouragement to make commitments beyond oneself, and opportunities for a steady deepening of self-insight. We believe these conditions to be genuinely essential: If the school can provide them, the chances for full growth are excellent; if it cannot, there will always be some crippling, some falling short of what might have been.

Perhaps some who read this will see in it an image of a soft, "idealistic" world where children are petted and pampered and *given* too much. We are so accustomed in these days to the harsher strains of talk of the *forcing* of growth, of a frenzied *pressure* upon youth, that anything else sounds weak and mild.

But our image is of another sort. It is an image of a child with a secure base to operate from as he forays out into a world that may be tough; a child with an accumulating reserve of experience that carries him courageously into new and risky ventures; a child with a concept of himself that nerves him to dare. It is anything but a soft and sentimental picture. For it assumes that life takes strength, and it is based on faith that a rugged inward strength can grow to a level of power most men never know they could have had.

THE ANTI-SCHOOL — SOME REFLECTIONS ON TEACHING

Jurgen Herbst

In teaching, as in everything that is important to us, nothing matters as much as our attitudes and our disposition. It is the frame of mind, the direction in which our mental as well as our emotional compass is set, that ultimately sustains us in our efforts and determines the effectiveness of our work. It is our deep-seated orientation toward life in all its aspects, intellectual and emotional, social and individual; an orientation that is revealed in a man's responses to the question: What is teaching to you? An opportunity to meet your needs and gratify your desires? A burden to be shouldered? A job you drifted into, or a profession freely chosen? A way to earn a living, or a way of life that commits you and your family with all your hopes for the future? In whatever answer a man may give—he reveals himself, his values, and his choices. He lets us see the things he cares for, and the intensity with which he cares for them.

Although refined by thought and made explicit in words, attitudes and disposition are not formed merely through intellectual exercises. Although they are hammered out and tempered in experience and their worth established and proved for us in daily tests and trials, they are not only reflex and habit. Attitudes and disposition arise from the thoughtful appraisal of experience, and indicate our conscious and personal acceptance of a way of life. Such acceptance is the result of the transmutation of experience through rational reflection

Reprinted from *Educational Theory*, Vol. 18 (Winter 1968), pp. 13–22, by permission of the publisher and Jurgen Herbst.

and emotional consent. What the discipline of education and the profession of teaching need today is neither more experience nor better definitions, but the reflective mastery of experience and its willed conversion into personal commitment. For the practical needs and concerns of teaching, pure experience is as worthless as the most refined learning, either singly or combined. It is when both experience and thought are charged with the energy of personal commitment, and when they thus nourish a man's attitudes and disposition that teaching achieves its fullest potentialities for teachers and their students alike.

This view of teaching, I am afraid, does not prevail in our schools and institutions of teacher training throughout the country. Much talk and many manifestos to the contrary, American teachers as a group do not impress the observer as constituting a profession conscious of its self-chosen objectives, standards, and aspirations, and committed to uphold and improve these. Rather, teachers resemble more what was once called "the hired clergy," a corps of specialists, ready to sell their talents, know-how, and skill to the highest or least demanding bidder, and ready, likewise, to adjust not only standards and aspirations, but also convictions and orientation to the demands of their employers. Proficiency in knowledge and skills are valued higher than the ability to judge discriminately in the choice of educational objectives, and to affirm one's choices in one's teaching. The hired teacher performs his tasks by adhering to manual or directive. He, in fact, invites these guidelines when, with no commitment of his own, he asks for and accepts the authority of others. To him teaching is a job, not a profession.

From college through graduate school, future teachers are told what, supposedly, they need to know to become competent teachers. This is to say, they are told what their teachers are able to tell them; what, in other words, teachers of teachers consider teachable. This is why in teacher training we emphasize so vigorously skills and techniques, materials and devices, doctrines and theories. We have focused our attention on that part of human experience and learning that can be transferred from man to man and handed down from generation to generation. Since such transfer obviously does take place, since its techniques can be acquired and transmitted, we have capitalized on this phenomenon, have called it education, and pronounced it to be a good thing. Our current national love-affair with it is about to drown us all in a flood of unexamined assumptions concerning teaching. It matters little whether we think of parents initiating their children into the mysteries of acceptable behavior, or of teachers in the classroom. In either case we think of adults telling children what to do. For the most part this telling consists of the indoctrination of various sorts of rules and laws, and it is judged to have been successful once the students know the rules and know how to apply them or live by them.

Education, in fact, has often been defined as the transmission of culture. Past knowledge and past experience is what one generation transfers to its successors. We may ask with Thoreau whether we have anything worth transmitting, anything that is worthy of transmission in its own right; and we may wonder, too, whether a thing that was once "useful and ornamental" (to use Benjamin Franklin's phrase) will be so for our children. We are all too keenly aware how much our desire to live forever spurs on our attempts at transmitting culture, how much our wish to have our children build monuments for us inspires our actions. When we as teachers allow our ambition to be stirred by this desire, we fasten the hold of the past over the future. We use teaching to fashion the young in the image of their elders, and we neglect to ask whether the perpetuation of this image is desirable. What right do we have to tell our children how to live? The earth belongs to the living, said Jefferson, yet we in our schools labor mightily to enshrine the past and deny the present. Is it any surprise when we learn from our historians that education nearly always has been a force that conserves, nay embalms, the past?

We all have learned in school or college that it was John Dewey and his disciples who broke the grip of the past over the present, who taught that each generation defines the world anew, just as it creates its own culture and rewrites history. Seen thus, education is not merely the transmission of past culture, but the continuing creation of present culture as well. It is, in its specific pedagogic function, the initiation of the young into the culture of the present. This kind of educational progressivism, we know, was a liberating force in its time; a great, welcome, and effective challenge to the thoughtless reiteration of statements and practices that no longer reflected current reality. John Dewey's reconstruction in education meant, in practice, education's attempted effort to reconstruct society and culture in and through the schools. Whatever one might think of such a program, it challenged teachers and children to forego the hand-me-down of rote learning, and to take an active part in the reconstruction of the world they lived in. It made science and the scientific method the chosen tools of this reconstruction, and shored up the reliance on science by asserting that science and democracy were born twins. The schools were to be the agents of cultural and social progress.

Unfortunately, progressivism fared no better than the traditionalism it replaced. It, too, succumbed rather quickly to its own orthodoxy and enshrined its dogmas and definitions. Teaching and instruction were exchanged for doing and activities; education meant learning how to live with others. Not the traditions of the past, but the incessant and ubiquitous voices of the present were accepted as authorities, and children were told—as one hapless educational philosopher put it recently—to see life patternwise. In David Riesman's apt phrase, we traded in our gyroscope for a radarscope. From an initial concern with the development of individuals, progressive education moved to the assimilation and integration of these individuals into society. What had started out as a promise of a new life in school and society ended up in the mindless worship of life adjustment. Where the traditionalist teacher of the late nineteenth century had been the spokesman for the respectability of the genteel tradition, the latter-day progressive adapted his students to the conformist style of middle-class suburbia. Where the nineteenth century had believed that academies, high schools, and colleges were to educate society's leaders and pacesetters, the twentieth century, being suspicious of claims to leadership, interpreted democracy to mean the homogeneity of the lonely crowd, and believed that schools should reflect this faceless society rather than challenge and reshape it. Thus the progressive reformer gave way to the other-directed man.

The latest phase of educational thought and practice reflects our current disillusionment with the progressivism of the life-adjusters and the traditionalism of advocates of memory learning. As set forth in Jerome Bruner's *Process of Education*, it represents an attempt to make respectable and respected again the academically oriented school by fashioning education in the image of scientific discovery, scholarly investigation, and theoretical understanding. The objective is neither the adjustment of individuals to their neighbors, nor the acquisition of factual information or technical skills, but the ability to think conceptually, to manipulate symbols, and to relate scientific theories to natural as well as social phenomena. Where once the more scientifically inclined among the progressives held that "to know something thoroughly involves knowing its quantity as well as its quality," their Brunerian successors maintain that knowledge is the "general understanding of the structure of subject matter." Such knowledge, to be sure, is the scientist's or the scholar's knowledge, and it has reference to the abstractions and symbol-systems we call theories. The aim of Bruner's process is to turn students into scientists, i.e., to teach them how through intellectual abstraction they may comprehend efficiently and comprehensively the varieties of human experiences, and how to translate such theoretical understanding into purposeful action. The way in which this objective is pursued leads through the laboratory or workshop where students are asked to rediscover for themselves what others have found before them, and through the lecture hall and library where students are asked to familiarize themselves with the "structures of subject matter" previously proposed, invented, or imagined.

Education as proposed by the Brunerians was a healthy corrective to the absurdities of life-adjustment. Yet we must realize that it aims to acquaint students with the scientists' representation of the world, not with the world itself. It is concerned with science, not with nature or man. The Brunerian theory of instruction rests squarely on the assumption that the scientific way of confronting and evaluating life is the most desirable one for all who live in the twentieth century. In our schools budding scientists and intellectuals of all persuasions readily respond, and we fare best in the college-preparatory classroom. Those of our students, however, who are less concerned with the validation of hypotheses, with inductive methodologies and scientific theories; who do not feel the urge or the necessity to dissect and analyze reality according to some scientific prescription; who are much more concerned with responding to reality in concrete situations rather than with knowing its structure; those students, I maintain, are ill served by the educational theory I have been discussing. They doubt that they can afford to learn and to know before they must act. In fact they know that action precedes knowing, and that the knowledge of structures is not more than a *post facto* rationalization of experience. They ask for experience, and the Brunerians give them definitions, the methodology of science, for all we know, may be a dead-end street for them. Who is to say that for them there are not other equally valid roads? Schools should provide the opportunity for the young to find their own way, not push them along the scientific super-highway we happen to prefer for ourselves.

The scientist's understanding of the structure of subject

matter is an effective way of knowing if one's aim is the manipulation and exploitation of the world. But, fortunately, men differ legitimately in their aims and aspirations, and not all of us either need or want to be scientists or scholars. This is a cheering thought when one considers how science is beset with its own orthodoxies and dogmas, and how salutary our skepticism toward scientific gospels may become. The Brunerians are already well on their way to endear to the interest of pedagogues words rather than things, concepts and theories rather than the realities of life. They teach subject matter rather than subjects, promise knowledge of life as interpreted in subject matter rather than the ability to lead happy lives. William James once expressed the matter well: "Knowledge of life is one thing; effective occupation of a place in life . . . is another." Life is too rich to be captured in subject matter, and the content of an academic curriculum tool limited to represent the raison d'être of a school. The Brunerians, in short, are out to shape students in their own image, mistaking themselves as part of the universe, for the whole of it.

Finally, one might point out that the notion of the structure of subject matter and its teachability does not touch on the structure of reality. The structure of subject matter is our inherited abstract of reality, and we find it easy to teach that which we ourselves have created by abstraction. Vico may be our guide who wrote: "And history cannot be more certain than when he who creates the things also describes them." Are we then to conclude since we did not create nature but only science, and since we did not create man but only wrote down his history, we cannot teach concerning nature and man, but only concerning science and history? The Brunerians, it appears, subscribe to this argument, since it is the structure of science and the structure of recorded history that they want to have taught in the schools. What is the structure of nature and of human events? Professor Bruner evades this question by referring us, not to history as events that happened, but to history as subject matter or to the social sciences. Recently he told us that history could not be studied for an understanding of structure—presumably he discovered that it had none—but "for the end of developing style." This admission undercuts his proud boast that through an understanding of structure any subject could be taught "in some intellectually honest form to any child at any stage of development." To school children who must live in the real world of history and to their teachers, the Brunerian doctrine with its emphasis on subject matter is of little help.

> I a stranger and afraid
> in a world I never made

What of the world and the history in which I live? This, it seems to me, is the real question asked by our children today, one which Professor Bruner leaves unanswered.

When I thus reject the definitions and aims of traditionalists, progressives, and Brunerians, what, you may ask, are we left with? What are the irreducible and undeniable elements of a situation in which human beings learn from one another, and in which this learning is neither the transmission of factual information nor the largely unconscious process of socialization or "growing up," nor indoctrination in the scientific methodology of structuring reality? How can teaching be free of social and conceptual constraints? How, on the teacher's part, may it again become the personal expression of informed commitment to the nurture of curious and creative minds in meaningful encounter with one another and with their surroundings? What happens, in other words, when mere experiencing and ratiocination give way to learning that is at once spontaneous and purposeful? Under what conditions can such teaching occur, and what are its chief characteristics?

All education begins with a question asked by one eager to learn. Learning then takes place when he who responds enables the questioner to arrive at the answer for himself. Teaching thus means to free people from their dependence on others, to stand them on their own feet, and to encourage them to walk for themselves. In other words: No more baby carriages, no more crutches, no more holding hands—Walk! Education begins with a question. If in their classroom students do not ask questions, it is not teachers we need, but drill sergeants or prison guards. A student is one who demands of his teachers: Show me how! Tell me why! Say what this is for! When teachers cease to hear and respond to these questions, when they no longer succeed in eliciting them, then their lectures and demonstrations have come to resemble those of salesmen and propagandists. It matters little whether teachers attempt to sell the facts of ancient history, the fashions of acceptable behavior, or the theories of nuclear physics. They are not responding to questions in the hope and with the intent that eventually the response becomes unnecessary and the student is able to answer his own questions. The objective of teaching is neither information, socialization, nor techniques, but the achievement of personal autonomy.

If one reflects on teaching in this manner, it quickly becomes apparent that neither traditionalists nor progressives and Brunerians view the teacher as one who responds to his students' questions. Rather they see him as the representative of society or as the scientific expert who tells his students what the authority of either society or science demands. Students who, for many and various reasons, are disposed to question this authority and who receive no hearing for their questions in the classroom, find schooling highly irrelevant and, sooner or later, rebel against it openly or covertly. In Darien where high school kids do as their elders do, they get killed or wind up in jail. In New York where they avoid doing as their elders do, they also get killed or wind up in jail. It is as Huck Finn observed: "What's the use you learning to do right, when it's troublesome to do right and ain't no trouble to do wrong, and the wages is just the same?" Authority no longer makes sense to him who is forced to grow up absurd.

Do those who cannot accept the authorities of society and science speak for today's students? Do the rebels represent fairly the American student of the mid-sixties? Do the teachers who sympathize with them and share their basic convictions express that which is vital and liberating in American education today? It is obvious, it seems to me, that the rebellious critics do not speak for the majority of either students or teachers. They do not now, as they have never done so in the past. They do, however, give shape and impetus to movements and styles in education, just as the more articulate spokesmen of the progressives and the Brunerians have done before them. Today's rebels, however, differ in one essential and decisive respect. They are leaving the schools rather than reforming them from within. High school students disappear before graduation, and college students, protesting the irrelevancy of much of their required course work, move out and set up their own "free universities," or get their education in Alabama, Vietnam, or the Peace Corps. They all turn their back on education as it is carried on and—as they believe—stifled in our institutions of learning, and they seek its essence in new surroundings. To the anti-hero of the anti-novel we can add, without unduly straining our metaphors, the anti-student of the anti-school: the drop-out in Vietnam, the civil rights worker in Mississippi, the so-called beatnik in the Village loft.

What, you may ask, is the anti-school? Where might we find it? The answer is clear: Wherever youths find relevance in their activities (whether registering Negro voters or discussing the ethics of love), wherever they face reality (whether among migrant workers, office secretaries, or inmates of prisons and mental hospitals), and wherever they must confront themselves (whether in the rice-paddies of Southeast Asia or on the picket line around the ammunitions plant), there is the anti-school. Wherever they are free to incorporate these and many similar experiences, either actual or vicarious ones, into their thoughts, emotions, and purposes without having to accept the structures and interpretations sanctioned by society or scholarship, there do they find their opportunities for an education that makes for personal autonomy. It is too much to ask that the anti-school may be found even in the classrooms of some of our schools? Is it too preposterous to suggest that perhaps, in time, the rebels among students and teachers will move back into the schools because they may find there what they had been searching for outside?

The aim of the anti-school is the fullest understanding of man's experience of the world. It is because experience is so freely and easily available, so overwhelming, diverse, and compelling, that the anti-school is not likely to suffer from lack of subjects. Students flock to it driven by a desperate need to master this experience, and mastery for them consists in ordering experience through structures and interpretations created by themselves. "Chaos is the law of nature, order is the dream of man," wrote Henry Adams, and in this sense, the students of the anti-school are dreamers. What they insist on is that they be allowed to dream their own dreams, not be forced to accept the dreams of their elders; to confront their own problems and order them in their own fashion, and not to be told to reshuffle the interpretations and structures of the past in the problem-solving exercises of so-called inductive teaching. The anti-school is not the swamp of anti-intellectualism as traditionlists and Brunerians try to make out. There are standards in the anti-school; standards that, it is true, are not upheld by the authority of the past, but by relevance to present and future needs, and, above all, by a concern for personal honesty, integrity, and consistency in the application of criteria for judgment. The anti-school teaches respect for subject, subject matter, and the man who beholds the subject and fashions the structure of the subject matter. It takes account of facts as they appear to the naked eye, as they are related by the probing intellect, and as they are then incorporated in a man's purposes and actions. The anti-school's contempt for purely academic knowledge of the world matches Jonathan Edwards' disdain of the merely notional knowledge of salvation, and the anti-school's insistence on personal commitment echoes Edwards' call for salvation's experimental and consenting knowledge. No one, as far as I know, has ever accused Edwards of anti-intellectualism. For the anti-school the fullest understanding of the world means objective, scientific knowledge of facts and relations, as well as personal, subjective commitment to these facts and relations. To know does not by itself mean either to accept or to reject. To know means to oblige the knower to do either. The anti-school, then, teaches its students to know the world as both observer and actor, both outsider and participant. It teaches that to live fully means to be both.

It is this quest for the fullest understanding of human experience, for the relevance of experience and knowledge to purposeful living that distinguishes the anti-school from the institutions we call schools today. We may decide, and I hope we will, that our schools might profit from the anti-schools, and we may feel that the anti-schools will provide the impetus for the revitalization of our schools. If so, we shall have to appreciate the lesson that real learning begins with the students' questions, rather than with the teacher's answers. We shall have to accept the idea that a teacher's answers are not for students to accept and memorize or even properly—i.e., with due respect for the niceties of parliamentary procedure or scientific logic—to debate, but to serve as examples not of what they assert, but of how assertions are made, how they may be improved, how they may assume relevance and meaning. How many of our so academically trained teachers have yet to learn that answers to questions or statements made by teachers are not always to be taken as challenges to verbal duel, factual fault-finding, or logic-chopping, but as invitations or inspirations for the students to formulate their own answers and statements? I am afraid that the premium placed in our schools on the facility with which a student juggles the structures and interpretations of subject matter has contributed to the students' mistaking notional knowledge for the knowledge of the world, and has produced the subsequent inevitable disillusionment that has fed the anti-schools. Students, we should remember, do not want answers from their teachers, but examples of how one goes about answering, and of how one's answers are made part of one's life. They do not want indoctrination in their facts, theories, or modes of behavior, but models of reality, interpretations, and styles, in order that they may have the opportunity of choosing among them discriminately, and of creating for their own needs the reality, structures, and attitudes that will enable them to live fully. Today's students know the fraud and dishonesty of so-called authoritative answers. They know, too, the brutality of honest questions, and they appreciate these questions, not because they are brutal, but because they are honest. Will we in our schools recognize the anguished cry for honesty, and will we be capable of responding to it?

I, for one, hope that the spirit of the anti-school might come alive in our classrooms to sweep out the vestiges of the progressives' other-directedness and the Brunerians' neo-traditionalism. I thus express my belief that, despite all I said, schools have a function and teachers a task. I believe that this function and task is to provide the conditions under which personal autonomy may emerge and be sustained, protected, and nurtured. I am convinced, however, that our schools today do not perform this function, and far too many teachers do not recognize their task, let alone carry it out. This is why so many of our youths search for themselves and their autonomy in the jungles of Vietnam and New York, drop out of suburbia and join up in Alabama, Nigeria, or Colombia. The schools have failed our youths, but they are thereby not doomed to persist in their failure. In this world of ever-increasing social pressures on children and adolescents, schools can be asylums for youths to grow into autonomous adults. As we have learned to protect our youngsters from economic exploitation in sweatshops and coal mines, we now must learn to protect them from the insidious pressures that demand grades, club memberships, and athletic records. In our schools we should have the golden opportunity of fostering the spirit of the anti-school in an environment that eliminates the intolerably high and cruel risks that are so much a part of the actual anti-school. It is a perverse sort of romanticism which argues that only the threat of bombs and bullets and the kick of drugs and drink will teach autonomy. Once we allow the spirit of the anti-school to enter our classrooms, once we become aware of the ritualistic nature of the claims of past scholarship and the equally ritualistic pressure of present-day social conventions, we may be in a position, as John Holt puts it, "to clear a space for honesty and openness and self-awareness in the lives of growing children." That, I should think, is a beginning if we are to restore our schools to meaning and relevance.

The dedication of our schools to their task of fostering and nurturing the growth of autonomous individuals depends for its success on the kind of teachers we shall find in them. This revitalization of which I have spoken is not a matter of administrative reform, but of pedagogical conviction on the part of the teacher. Administrators cannot order it, although they can stimulate and encourage it. What counts are the attitudes and the disposition of the teacher. Teachers must practice what they preach. If teachers want their students to bring their questions into the classroom, and if they urge their students to question and requestion the answers they receive, then the teachers themselves must be the first to insist on further questions, and to refuse to accept or to propose answers in such a manner as forecloses further questioning. If teachers want students to rely on the evidence of their own experience, then they must do so themselves. Teachers must not allow theories of education, of human nature, and of subject matter to stand between them and what they see. They must have the courage to trust their own eyes and ears, rely on their own thinking, and follow their own insights to their results, instead of citing the authorities of, say, Karl Marx, Sigmund Freud, or John Dewey. They must take theories for what they are: aids to our understanding, not substitutes for it, designed to simplify reality and to present it to our view one-dimensionally, as a map represents a landscape. Let not teachers mistake the map for the landscape, and their students' ability to read a map for their skill in finding their way. Let them be autonomous themselves to be able to distinguish that which is real from that which is its copy or representation. If we want autonomous students, we must first have autonomous teachers.

This brings me back to my initial concern with a teacher's attitudes and disposition. A teacher teaches as he is, that is to say, he teaches by his personal example. It should give us pause to note how dullness breeds dullness, and enthusiasm inspires the love of learning. Think of the second-grade teacher whom John Holt quotes as saying: "But my children *like* to have questions for which there is only one answer." "They did," adds Holt, "and by a mysterious coincidence, so did she." Teachers must live their teaching in order that their attitudes and disposition do the teaching that needs to be done. If creativity is the constructive response to situations, and this response be creative rather than imitative, then it is not to models, theories, and structures that we must look, but to the energies, styles, and orientations that produced these models, theories, and structures in the first place. We do not need schools today to teach people how to perform jobs. We need schools to enable people to create jobs, and to endow their existence with meaning.

For teachers all of this insists on one commandment: Be honest, genuine, and real; speak for yourself. Once your students perceive that you practice the autonomy you preach, that you refuse to be society's or scholarship's mouthpiece, they will let you teach them. Affirm and protect your autonomy and know that once you have lost it, you have lost your ability to teach, whatever your certificate, your title, or your reputation. Remember, too, that autonomy does not mean the principled rejection of authority, but rather the ability to accept or reject in the light of your own consistent standards. Once your students know your commitment to autonomy, they will accept your teaching of the authorities of society, scholarship, and science, because they will know by your example that honest men can be committed to traditional and shared values critically and sincerely. They will have learned that the flaming No of adolescent rebellion is not the same as the committed No of principled autonomy. And, judging by so many of our adolescent escapists from both suburbia and slum, this may be a lesson well worth learning or, in your case, teaching.

Let me close, then, by emphasizing the real as opposed to the academic character of meaningful education. If we have in the past largely seen schooling as preparation, and children as miniature adults; as, with the progressives, we have forced them into the accepted modes of adult behavior; and as, with the Brunerians, we regard them all as future scientists and intellectuals, we deny them the reality of their actual existence. It has taken open rebellion and violent protest to open our eyes to facts which should have been obvious; namely, that teenagers, whether black or white, in city slums or country homes will not eagerly and positively respond to an education that is designed to prepare them for a life they will never lead. They know it, their teachers know it; yet their teachers keep on teaching "by the book." That kind of book-education, let me assure you, is absurd. What's worse, the absurdity transfers itself onto both students and teachers. The students, to their credit, rebel and quit; the teachers complain and carry on— a difference that does not speak well for the teaching profession. But there you are again. When will teachers trust their own eyes and sense? When will they take a theory or a text-book for what it is, namely, an aid that disqualifies itself the very minute it no longer aids? When will they speak for themselves? When will they quit transmitting a culture they cannot live with, quit accepting an authority they cannot but question, and when will they begin consciously and willingly to participate in the creation of a culture that all of us can live in?

PART II

What is Individualization?

Self-selection, self-direction with responsibility, self-actualizing autonomous individuals—What do they mean for instruction? How does a classroom function? Children making decisions, inquiry and direct interaction with primary sources of information, a focus on how to learn instead of learning? What is the framework? What are the restrictions?

Individualization for many people calls to mind a one-to-one teacher-student ratio. But the number of people involved, whether it be one or thirty-five, is not the heart of the matter. Group teaching is both necessary and desirable as are individual pupil-teacher conferences. What then are the critical points? Can individualization of instruction be a strategy which is entirely teacher-controlled? What is the role of the pupil? Is individualization only a means with no relationship to ends? These are only some of the questions to be examined as the teacher begins a careful study of what individualization is.

INDIVIDUALIZED INSTRUCTION: FORM AND STRUCTURE

Virgil M. Howes

To clarify individualization of instruction as a strategy for teaching and as a basis for organizing a school is a formidable task. Attention and research efforts have emerged from a variety of sources in the attempt to lift the quality of American education. Each has helped to shape and to add to the meaning of the concept. But with the different underlying assumptions and the different focuses for probing, there have been gaps and divergencies.

Three efforts which have added power and impetus to the search for meaning of individualization of instruction have been the curriculum reform movement, the development of technology adaptable to education, and concern for the disadvantaged pupil and the concomitant desegregation moves.

Immediately after World War II, curriculum remaking became a major concern. Content was added and updated; subject matter was reorganized, frequently around the structural elements of a discipline; and new instructional packages were developed. The principle of individual differences was recognized not only in the quantity and range of materials to meet interest and ability needs, but also in the instructional strategies emphasized. Some curriculum reform attempts appeared to focus on ways to make materials teacher-proof. Others, however, directly challenged existing instructional

Adapted from *Individualization of Instruction: A Search*, Los Angeles, California, [ASUCLA Students' Store, 308 Westwood Plaza], 1967, pp. 53–73.

practices, and project staffs developed extensive in-service teacher education programs. Clearly, curriculum reformers recognized that program efforts had to be directed toward making teachers interested in using the new materials and using them according to the underlying functions and concepts.

Technology became another major force behind the school's attempt to individualize instruction. The early teaching machines as well as today's computers provide valuable hardware capable of handling instructional programs geared to specific abilities, needs, progress, and interests of individuals. But the full capabilities of available technologies are still to be recognized because software developments lag far behind hardware advancements.

Most of the current computer-assisted instruction is based on programmed instruction. Such instruction typically deals with individual differences in a limited way—chiefly by permitting students to move as slowly or as rapidly as they can through the same material. The current research in programming suggests, however, that we have been mistaken in thinking present programming allows students to "learn at their own rate." Experiments reveal that when programmed materials are arranged more flexibly, and the learner is trained to use them in whatever way suits his learning needs, learning is faster than when he must go through an instructor-programmed sequence of material. The increased capability of modern, available hardware, while offering potential aid in accounting for individual differences, raises even more forcefully the question of how instruction is to be individualized.

A third major force in the effort to clarify individualization of instruction has been the desegregation efforts of the schools and the focus on the disadvantaged pupil. Typically, the children affected by these programs perform at lower levels and need additional help to overcome past failures. If we group these children simply on the basis of performance, we re-segregate and fail to bring them into the mainstream of school life. Clearly, an alternative is needed as we search for a solution. There is need for a system of instruction which fits each learner and the educational task to be accomplished. The concept of individualization of instruction offers such a possibility.

While these and other forces have emphasized the importance of individualization and provided a variety of definitions and practical examples, little consensus has been produced. An analysis and examination of predominant characteristics, bases for decisions, underlying assumptions of these definitions reveal three major modes of individualized instruction. It is to a description of each of these we now turn.

ADJUSTED INSTRUCTION

Historically, "adjusted instruction" was probably the first major attempt to individualize. As America's great experiment in mass education developed, schools became graded, and materials were written to correspond to this organization. A lockstep curriculum evolved organized on the basis of adult interests and needs. It was in this setting that early attempts to individualize instruction began and continue even today. Plans, largely administrative, are advanced for better adjustment of the schools toward individual pupils—shortening the interval for reclassification of children, organizing special classes, developing parallel track plans, and altering retention and acceleration procedures.

Many developments are attempts to group children in ways that reduce the range of differences. For example, special classes for the mentally retarded were the first provisions, but over the years the organization and kinds of special classes began to expand. To classes for the mentally retarded were added special classes for the gifted, the physically handicapped, the emotionally disturbed, and others. For some pupils, supplementary or enrichment classes were opened. These have been attempts by the school system to provide for in-

individual differences through administrative organizations and adjustments which hopefully organize learners more homogeneously.

Other efforts to adjust instruction focus on classroom grouping plans. The three-group plan for reading instruction, for example, is a popular method to adjust instruction for individuals. For instruction in other subject areas, children in the class may be grouped on the basis of achievement, interest, or reading level.

Newer developments today are focusing on other adjustments. The effectiveness of homogeneous grouping has raised doubts and the self-contained classroom with one teacher is questioned. Recommendations include plans for nongrading, multigrading, and team teaching. These plans are more sophisticated attempts to reorganize the school's structure, to eliminate artificial progression barriers, and to facilitate a different curriculum organization.

In adjusted instruction, the elements of the system or the classroom are altered in an attempt to reach the individual learner more successfully. Some attempts focus on draining off, rearranging, or in some way reducing the more extreme differences within a group. Newer attempts promote more open structure and less rigidity in school organizational patterns. Instructional talent is deployed in larger units rather than one teacher to a class. But, hopefully, the structure and elements of the school setting are altered to facilitate teacher efforts to individualize instruction.

DIFFERENTIATED INSTRUCTION

In the second mode of individualized instruction, emphasis is placed on accounting for individual differences in designing teaching and carrying on its purposes. Such instruction has as its core not only a focus on the variety and ranges of individual differences; but it also emphasizes the role of the teacher in providing for, dealing with, and meeting or accommodating instruction to these differences. We call this mode "differentiation of instruction."

In differentiation of instruction methods, techniques and procedures have more commonly focused on the ranges of individual differences in such dimensions as rate of learning, general ability, and pupil interest. Early proposals, such as the Winnetka Plan and the Dalton or Contract Plan, as well as recent proposals, have emphasized rate of learning or pacing as the key individual difference to be accommodated. The learner in some way or other is free to move ahead through common programs and materials as fast as he can. He may work independently of other class members, receiving teacher help as needed, until the work assignment has been completed or mastery attained.

Since the concept of rate has grown within the context of gradedness and with its implications, most attempts to provide for this difference retain the concept of "coverage of specified material." In fact, freedom to proceed at one's own rate frequently implies that the amount of work must be done within a particular grade: a school year. If a student progresses rapidly and completes the "required amount," he can then proceed with "enrichment material."

Today, most programmed learning is built around the key element of pacing. The material to be learned is laid out in series of bite-sized, sequential steps, and the learner progresses on the basis of correct responses at his own speed. However, as pointed out earlier, this procedure may in effect slow students down, since they must work through materials which have been sequenced in such amounts as to make it possible for even the slow student to accomplish the task. Undoubtedly, then, some students must proceed through much more material than is actually necessary for them to grasp particular concepts or skills.

Continuous progress plans are other forms for recognizing and accounting for individual differences in speed of learning. Grade levels are no longer barriers to the amount of learning accomplished in a specified time; nor is coverage of specified blocks of materials demanded in six weeks, two months, or another prescribed time period. Again, the differentiation provided for continuous progress is largely focused on the element of speed of learning rather than on what is to be learned.

The ability of the learner has been a second major difference emphasized in differentiated instruction. Plans focus on altering sequence or content on an individual basis, the use of different books and materials to provide for a range in ability, varying the nature of individual assignments, deferment of beginning work in a skill such as reading, and other adaptations of instruction to individuals with many levels of competence and ability.

A third difference recognized in plans for differentiating instruction has been children's interests. Sometimes, interest has served as a basis for grouping, independent study, or selection of materials. Capable teachers have utilized learner interest as a strong motive for learning.

But individual differences in learning are more numerous and diverse than the dimensions which have accounted for most of our attempts to differentiate instruction. We are only beginning to develop understandings of some differences, such as learning styles or patterns. Researchers have identified intricate visual, aural, and physical learning styles. Other dimensions that they have noted include flexibility—the ease with which a learner can shift meaningfully from one learning task to another, amount of pressure and its stimulation or negation of learning results, and rate of speed.[1] There are differences in motivational patterns for individual learners. How do learners respond to various reward systems? Psychological research is contributing much which should provide us newer and better ways to differentiate instruction. We can see a progression in differentiation of instruction. There are new and dynamic attempts to use the latest knowledge from theory and research to create meaningful strategies of instruction in which teachers

[1] Frank Riessman, "The Strategy of Style," *Teachers College Record*, March 1964, pp. 484–489.

are consciously making decisions. The latest knowledge from learning theory, rather than intuitive feelings, is being used to custom-tailor an educational prescription for the individual learner.

Differentiation of instruction has a long and important history. We are only beginning to see the power of differentiated instructional strategies based on psychological and learning theory. To date, efforts have been applied mostly in the facts and skills segment of our curriculum. These programs and plans, and new ones being tested, may some day largely free us from a segment of education or training which has dominated us too long in the schools. If these approaches provide success we may have room for other dimensions in teaching.

But, we must ask ourselves: What happens when teachers begin to apply new strategies to developing attitudes, interests, ethical and moral beliefs, feelings, the behavior of the "good citizen," or "pursuing the good life?"

The differentiated instructional strategies used for facts and skills will work, but now our content is different. Our subject matter is basic individual beliefs. These instructional strategies now seem to slip over into the arena of indoctrination[2] rather than differentiation of instruction. What then is to be the nature of our teaching communication with the child? How are we to individualize instruction?

INDIVIDUALIZATION—A FOCUS ON INDEPENDENCE AND SELF-DIRECTION

For the two modes of individualization of instruction just described, consideration is largely focused on individual differences as the primary base of decisions for strategy development. We think about individualization of instruction in terms

[2] See John Wilson, "Education and Indoctrination," Chapter II, *Aims in Education: The Philosophic Approach*, ed. by T.H.B. Hollins (Manchester, England: Manchester University Press), 1964.

of meeting, caring for, providing for, adjusting to individual differences. This language describes the expected teacher behavior. It is the teacher who meets, cares for, provides for individual differences among pupils in the class. Teacher decision and direction are predominant. This emphasis on individual differences and teacher responsibility has, I think, restricted our thinking about the concept and narrowed our vision.

A third mode of individualized instruction expands the concept and attempts to include other important dimensions. In part, it grows out of a simple restatement of our concern: how to maximize individual development in a democratic society:

1. We note that the concern is not with differences but with individual development and becoming.
2. Our concern relates to societal goals for the functioning of the individual. These goals stress the development of individuals who are self-directive, self-disciplined, self-responsible, and capable of making intelligent choices.
3. We believe that ends and means are interwoven and inseparable. One must be coordinated with the other. If we state a desire to develop a self-responsible learner, then our means must not be such that responsibility is taken away. How can a child become self-directing if our means are such that decisions related to his learning are made by another?
4. Last, we are guided by the belief that virtually every child needs, and can substantially benefit from, a mode of instruction which gives more autonomy to the learner.

These are the bases for the mode of individualized instruction which emphasizes learner autonomy. We seek then an instructional strategy in which a person can investigate and discover for himself; a mode of teaching which increases learner direction and control; and management procedures and arrangements which match individual development with larger and larger amounts of self-selection, self-guidance, and learner responsibility.

With this frame of reference, the teacher's instructional role takes on these characteristics:

1. *The teacher moves away from being a transmitter of knowledge toward behaving as a responder controlled by the pupil.* The object is to make teaching responsive rather than directive. The teacher follows student directions and demands even if the teacher considers them to be inadequate. This may be a painful role. The teacher may not be able to give all the information in a particular sequence because the learner decides to turn off the flow. But the reward comes from observing a child cross the threshold of learning.

2. *The teacher moves away from being the initiator-developer toward being a contributor-reactor.* The intent is clear. In traditional schools, teachers do most of the initiating with pupils reacting. Without fully realizing it, the teacher takes over the impossible task of being responsible for the pupil's learning. We all acknowledge that learning goes on all the time without formal, directed instruction. But somehow when the school bell rings, the thought gets pushed aside. Once again, our approach reveals our attitude that the learner himself knows nothing about what is good for him. But, in this strategy for individualizing instruction, the roles are not only reversed but new depth in meaning is intended. For it is no longer an approval-disapproval reaction; it is an exchange which adds and expands on initial learner efforts, an interaction focused toward development. It is an active, not a passive role. Facts are presented to help pupils form decisions. Attempts are made to help the pupil gain a conscious awareness of aspects of his feelings and desires which he may not see or realize. Learning plans are first evaluated not as a product but on the logic, rationality, and data used in development. The evaluation of the plan as a product comes after its imple-

mentation. The teacher's role focuses on the expansion of learner growth in self-direction and critical analysis by the pupil of his progress.

3. *The teacher moves away from being a programmer-director toward being a co-designer-assister.* It is doubtful that we as teachers can ever know the step-by-step learning needs of the numerous pupils with whom we interact. And, in the long run, it is the learner who needs to build up the data bank of this information. Since the learner is the person most vitally concerned in the educative process, it is he who must gain greater and greater understanding and insight into his functioning as a learner. Our intent is for the learner to build techniques of effective inquiry and to gain confidence and skills in attacking new learning problems. The teacher's pre-plans focus on such decisions as (a) what books, films, materials, and other components need to be put into the environment; (b) which children he needs to confer with; (c) general class or small group plans and arrangements he wants to discuss. The teacher constantly reviews and evaluates the effectiveness of the array of choices and the interacting engagement of pupils in learning activities and processes.

Different teachers will have different instructional styles since they too are individuals. But even with teaching-style adaptations, management procedures and arrangements found in classrooms emphasizing learner autonomy in individualization of instruction have certain characteristics. Affecting all operations will be conditions built on the basic premise that, since the learner is the person most vitally concerned in the educative process, it is he who must gain greater and greater understanding and insight into his functioning as a learner. He must gain skill and precision in assessing himself. There is a framework of elements made up of the following:

1. The school and teaching will emancipate the student from a dependence upon a system, whether it be the method

of teaching, the organization of the school, or the structure of the program. There will be a consistency between the schooling process and the elements of belief, trust, and value for the individual. Teaching will focus on integrative behaviors rather than directive behaviors.

2. Pupils will have freedom to make real choices and decisions in learning in at least these areas:

goals—what is to be learned
means—plans, strategies, techniques for learning
organization and management of individual learning plans
materials and aids for learning
evaluation—a look at what they did, how it worked, what needs changing, what needs doing

3. The alternatives provided in a school setting will be free of any imposed punishment or reward. The child's self-esteem will be nurtured, not graded or ranked. Psychological manipulation through imposed reinforcement either by a teacher or the system may produce training but it does little to create an individual who can function more and more as an architect of self. There will be an atmosphere where children can afford to change, to reconsider perceptions and to integrate them. The climate will enable a child to discard or test a value without losing face—a climate where one can admit error and not be defenseless.

4. The program, the curriculum, will capitalize on life's drama as the basis for learning. It will focus on increasing the resources of the individual, of enlarging his repertory of possible actions, of improving perceptions. It will be relevant as viewed by the learner and focused on learning to live. The child's curriculum is likely to be the observations of phenomena, social events, ideas in books, and so forth. There must be opportunity for pupils to confront their own problems and order them in their own fashion. Teaching the child to see what is in the environment is by no means the same as teaching him the environment in the form of a number of subjects.

These are some of the guidelines for a strategy of individualization of instruction which recognizes each child's own desire to discover, to explore, and to react to stimuli in his environment. Certainly we need to add to our map and plot our route in more detail. Here we need experiments and more research. To what extent can the learner take over the task of goal setting, the task of sequencing learning, the task of self-management? Is this mode of individualized instruction the best for all situations? For all needs and requirements?

CONCLUSION

We have looked at three modes of individualized instruction. We have examined each to a limited extent. One seems to focus on adjusting elements of the system or creating new structures permitting conditions of freedom for teachers to try various methods. A second emphasizes teacher direction, conscious decision-making based on appropriate data and knowledge, and focused primarily on means. Individual differences form the primary base for developing a strategy. A third challenges us to think in terms of individual development and becoming, not differences. It demands that we consider not only the sum of the characteristics of qualities that sets one person apart from others but also the goal or end desired for the development of the individual in a democratic society. It emphasizes learner autonomy, control, and self-direction. This mode of individualized instruction raises questions like these:

1. Do children have a daily diet of making big as well as little decisions in their learning?
2. Do the decisions pupils make really count? Are they valued? Do they serve as a basis for action?
3. Are pupils truly partners with teachers in the schooling endeavor?

4. Are we putting to work in the classroom a basic belief in the democratic process through which a free people can find their own best way to solve problems, to achieve goals?
5. Are we effectively harnessing the learner's energy for his own best interests?

It is time, I think, that we give full meaning to the concept of individualization of instruction as we practice teaching. It is time that we seriously pursue a concept of individualization of instruction which places trust in the learner and uses his energy for his learning.

RESEARCH THEMES
IN INSTRUCTIONAL
THEORY

Nathaniel H. Moore

Three main thrusts seem evident in research in instructional theory. These thrusts are likely to continue to develop during the next twenty years. In order to examine these movements it is necessary to oversimplify their independence of each other. Actually, these thrusts overlap each other to a considerable extent and are not as discrete in form as a writer would like them to be.

The first of these thrusts can be identified as the body of research based on the programmed approach to education and on the reinforcement work done by B. F. Skinner.

A second thrust is in the area of structural analysis and has its base in the work of Piaget. Both deal with the cognitive level of learning and with the new insight we have gained in recent years in the cognitive development in children. Further, both deal with structural analysis of the curriculum and with a similar analysis of the teaching act.

A third main thrust, which the writer believes is readily identifiable in instructional research at the present time, deals with the affective domain and is traceable to work that has been done by followers of Carl R. Rogers, and is reflected primarily in the work of Arthur W. Combs.

Let us attempt to establish as a fact that these thrusts do

From *Educational Leadership*, Vol. 26, No. 2, November 1968, pp. 154–57. Reprinted with permission of the Association for Supervision and Curriculum Development and Nathaniel H. Moore. Copyright © 1968 by the Association.

exist and are identifiable. They are also, to a certain extent, at odds with one another regarding what they believe education should do and how this should be done.

RESEARCH BASED ON SKINNER'S WORK

There is already a thrust of instructional theory research which is an outgrowth of B. F. Skinner's work. This theme of development is, incidentally, purer in its delineation than are the other two themes. Perhaps this is a result of B. F. Skinner's conceptualizing the process of education in oversimplified terms as he has sought to bring additional insight to the field of education regarding instructional theory. Skinner's theme emphasizes the concept of individualized learning and immediate reinforcement as the primary touchstone in the work that he has done. Through this work we see the development of programs for pacing cognitive learning at various rates and the provision of reinforcement for the student when he correctly responds to the problem with which he is presented.

Skinner is joined in his pursuit by a very impressive array of industrial giants interested in the field of education, a substantial portion of the U.S. Office of Education, and some of the practicing professionals in the field of psychology. The strength of this theme seems to be its efficiency. When promoters wish to impress one with the possibilities of their theories, they discuss the rate at which they have been able to teach people certain bodies of content.

A second strength of this particular theory is that it describes more specifically what it intends to do and is able to submit scientific evidence for having reached its objective. This again gives Skinner's theory power in a political sense on the modern education scene, for both efficiency of operation and scientific proof of successfully completing that operation have great power in our land. The critics of this particular thrust recognize the efficiency of the individual pacing and programs and the immediate reinforcement, but suggest that the use of this theory is limited to a small portion of the total process of educating the child and, while it can be useful, particularly in cognitive skills development, its use will remain of minor importance.

The promoters of this thrust do not agree. They feel that as their research matures, they will be able to program the total educational process. As their research matures with computer-assisted programming and systems analysis, they believe they will be able to invade the higher levels of the cognitive domain as well as the affective domain. Future implications for instructional theory, as far as this theme is concerned, see the teacher as primarily a diagnostician who will act as a prescriber of programs for each child.

During the next twenty years it is likely that this thrust in educational research, as far as the promoters are concerned, will develop what will represent a total program of instruction. We will see some computerized schools with programs which will seek to affect both the higher and lower cognitive levels and the affective domain. The homes of students who attend these schools will probably have a considerable amount of individual pacing paraphernalia, and the teacher will be seen primarily in the role of diagnostician. The power of this thrust will, in my opinion, however, diminish in direct proportion to its use. The writer believes that this theme of research has conceived education too narrowly to be accepted by any substantial portion of the nation. Followers of this school of thought have seemed to overemphasize the importance of cognitive development in a dependent manner that may, as far as the affective domain is concerned, dangerously approach brainwashing. Further, they have failed to comprehend the education of the child as a socialization force, as a force of conserving the society for which the child is being educated. As their failure to deal with the total educational process becomes more apparent, their support will diminish.

Any practicing educator is aware that a system may do a

poor job of teaching the skills with only the mildest of reprimands. Yet, when a school system deals inadequately with the socialization of the child, particularly in relation to conserving the society, the educator is in trouble. This theory has a weakness in its development of dependency which should be considered more seriously by educators. Probably the worst aspect of our present educational program is in its development of a dependent relationship which tends to produce weak people, which in turn will produce a weak society. The development of children who are independent in their thought and action must, in the writer's opinion, be one of our prime criteria in evaluating the positive effect of instructional theory.

EFFECTS OF PIAGET'S WORK

Piaget's analysis of intellectual growth has, in the writer's opinion, captured the imagination of a much wider audience than was expected or deserved and has resulted in others applying his findings in ways that may have been unwarranted by the original work. Let us assume here that Piaget's conclusions about the development of intellectual behavior are sound, for it would take at least another article to question effectively the research he has submitted regarding the intellectual growth of a child. Most of the body of instructional theory that is being developed on the theme of structural analysis finds its base in Piaget's work. We have, as a consequence, a great array of projects which have been funded by foundations and the U.S. Office of Education. These projects attempt to analyze the structure of various disciplines with the idea that, by having scholars develop a basic structure for their discipline and by coordinating this structure with the work of psychologists in analyzing the intellectual development of the child, we will develop an instructional program which may challenge the optimum learning power of the child.

The power of this body of research lies, the writer believes, in the weaknesses of the previous curriculum. Much of the traditional content in schools has been poorly thought through, poorly organized, and has resulted in teaching of half-truths and even material that was completely contrary to fact. Whenever the public school curriculum is analyzed by scholars in any special field, it has been found severely wanting. It seems that this field of research should improve this situation immensely as it continues over the next ten or twenty years. However, the strength of research is also its weakness. As this movement contributes to the improvement of the content of the curriculum, it will lose power, for it has again conceived the process of education too narrowly. Perhaps its greatest weakness is that the promoters of this work seem to believe that the child learns that which is taught.

The writer once heard a man suggest that if a child learned, during his educational experience, no more than what was taught in the public school, he would know so little that he would have to be institutionalized upon ending his association with the school. Further, the promoters of this instructional theory have seen the acquisition of content as the primary purpose of the public school and have seemed to comprehend little of the importance of this acquisition as a socializing force. They seem to view knowledge as a possession, rather than as a tool to be used. Also, this group is doing little better than the immediate-reinforcement people by way of providing for the development of independence on the part of the child as he goes through the process of being educated. It should be noted, however, that as this group proceeds to test materials its members are beginning to see that there is no one best way of structuring the curriculum, and that students will not obtain the insight they wish with one particular approach. As this group proceeds in the future, I would expect its members to develop more flexibility in their development of instructional programs and gradually begin to see how they have underrated the importance of the teacher and his relationship to what is learned. They will, I believe, be able to see that the idea of "teacher-proof" curriculums was simply juvenile and, if their programs are to have any success, these will have to be adapted to the teacher's strengths.

EFFECTS OF COMBS' WORK

Arthur W. Combs' work on instructional theory will, in the writer's opinion, have a great deal of power, if those who utilize his work are wise enough to incorporate into it the materials and programs that have been developed by the other researchers already mentioned. Combs' power is his recognition of the importance of developing independently strong people in a society that is rapidly becoming more relativistic and ambiguous. When societies are simplistic and absolute, strong frameworks are put up for weak and dependent people which allow them to function effectively. As a society becomes more complex and less absolute, more relative, more ambiguous, and less structured, ever stronger people must develop if they are going to be able to function effectively. Combs recognizes this fact in his work and has made progress in demonstrating to the practitioner in the field what the important ingredients of this process are and how the process can be implemented.

Combs recognizes an important principle that seems to have bypassed the other main thrusts of research on the current educational scene. He realizes that we value people for their likenesses and, because of this respect we have for the worth and the dignity of the human, we seek to analyze and meet man's individual needs as a human being. Thus, individualization is not an end in itself, but a part of a process. Those who miss the implications of this very important point are apt to do much more to weaken education than to strengthen it. From this base, an educator can work to overcome the dehumanizing forces that exist in society, and can overcome the denaturing process that Bruner refers to and, thus, eliminate accepting this process as a fact of life as Bruner does. The strength of Combs' research points to the importance of how one feels about himself as a determiner of what he will learn, how great his insight will be, and what functional use he will be able to make of his own learnings and insights.

During the next twenty years, the writer believes, this theme will grow in power as the society becomes more aware of the need for the type of man this process of education will produce in order for the society to function effectively. If this, in fact, does not happen. Orwell's prediction of a 1984 may very well become a reality.

Another power of Combs' work has to do with his flexibility of operation and the role he projects for the teacher. As his research progresses, we will see the teacher emerge as a more powerful figure. As we begin to understand more completely the interaction between the student and teacher and the effect of this interaction on the child's development of self-concept, the writer believes we will see the teacher becoming more and more crucial in the child's healthful development. The evidence to this point suggests that, with wholesome development, the child's capacity to learn is vastly accelerated over what might be done with simply well-developed curriculum materials or intricately paced programs with their immediate reinforcements.

Combs' research also suggests the liberating effect of such an approach upon the child. It seems to improve the child's opportunity to learn *more* than is being taught, for it develops him as an independent person. The other themes of research, however, tend to develop his dependence upon systems of education. It is the writer's opinion that we will see an ever-growing power in instructional theory when that theory weans the child from its system rather than encourages his dependence on the system. It would seem extremely difficult to argue that curriculum materials or other gadgetry can promote independence as well as an insightful teacher can if given the proper background and opportunity.

Future research in instructional theory, the writer believes, will have the greater power when that research concentràtes on the humanizing elements in education and on independence from the system by which the educational process is guided. The writer has tried to suggest that much of current instructional theory, which is not directed toward these aims, must be altered drastically in the light of Combs' work. The overall picture of research and instructional theory, however, is a very positive one.

In spite of the proliferation of weaknesses in the programs we have developed, we have demonstrated our ability to conceptualize the process of education that has been needed by our society in the past. This may have some predictive value as we try to conceptualize the process of education that is needed by our society now and in the future.

INDIVIDUALIZING

Jeannette Veatch

Individualizing is a way to think about managing the classroom. It is *not* a method of instruction. It is the way a teacher arranges children, equipment, and materials so that each child can learn eagerly at the peak of his potential, without undue stress and strain.

Thus geography can be "individualized" even though the entire class is seated in rows and the teacher is telling them, as a whole, about the islands in the Caribbean. Music can be individualized, too, when one group of children is holding on to *do*, another is sustaining *mi*, and a third group is being helped to hear how *sol* sounds when it is right.

Individualization is a philosophy that can take many forms in the schoolroom. It isn't its shape that counts, it is what happens to each child that counts. The learning will come bubbling hot when things are right. But what makes them right? Go back to the examples above.

The teacher telling about islands in the Caribbean is holding the attention of the entire class—not because he is lecturing on a chapter in the social studies text, but because the children are puzzled by the onslaught of the news about the Dominican Republic. To individualize teaching, should he tell every child singly, in turn, about the islands of the Caribbean? Of course not! It would waste time and therefore taxpayers' money. Telling the whole class *is* individualized teaching when the teacher is striking the hot iron of group interest.

Go back to the music experience. Why is this an example of individualization? To sing a chord with one's peers is a real

Reprinted and adapted from *The Instructor*, September, October, December 1965, and January 1966, by permission of the author and the publisher.

thrill. The *sol* group is off key. Every single child in all three groups is on a hot seat of auditory anguish until the dissonance is resolved. This "fitting" of sound cannot occur if each child, or each group, sings alone. All must sing together and the teacher must move the errant tones up or down until the peace of the fit comes. Then is each child enthralled with the part he played in making that chord a whole. Each one has discovered individually the pleasure of doing something exactly right.

These two are not examples of what is usually considered individualized learning. That is why they were chosen. Most teachers know about one-to-one conferences in reading, though they may never use them. Such conferences, unless they are taken seriously, can be corrupted into laissez-faire, structured, every-one-is-asked-the-same-question type, regardless of the fact that each child reads from a different book. There is no reason to have separate sessions on a one-to-one basis if a teacher uses the time to ask each child the same questions general enough to suit all circumstances. . . .

Individualization is, above all other things, a human act. Materials are important, surely, but they do not dictate. Plans are important, of course, but they cannot be determined before the teacher sees his charges. Schedules, in the same way, cannot be ignored, but bells, in the halls or in the teacher's head, cannot control the starting and stopping of learning.

No man is an island. Isolation of individuals should not occur in the classroom. Yet, how often teachers see a series of one-to-one conferences as the only way to individualize! It isn't the one-to-oneness that counts. It isn't the two-ness, or the group-ness or the class-ness. It is what happens between the human beings in that schoolroom that counts!

When a teacher and a child do sit down for a discussion in any learning area, conditions are ripe for real education to take place. But there is no guarantee!

When human interaction takes place on a level where each respects the other's thoughts and ideas, we are getting close to the secret of truly meeting individual differences. It is always a matter of degree. How close do you come?

SOME GROUND RULES

The best way to meet individual differences is in the "one teacher, one child" situation, but since to consider this as a possibility under present conditions is idealistic and impractical, what form of individualization can be practiced? First, let us consider what is the heart of individualization. Put simply, it is the extent to which a pupil has a choice over what he does during school hours. Children can and do commit themselves to learning when it is important to them. Yet we have areas of curriculum that must be covered, or uncovered, as the case may be. The answer is to leave curriculum-based activities open-ended so each child can find his own beginning spot, rate of progress, and stopping point.

Teachers who are not ready to try an approach that has no structure should recognize that there can be structure in a program stressing individualization and that it can free the teacher. For example, the teacher can follow the spelling book to the dot or he can note errors in his pupils' independent writing and draft a class list of spelling words for the next week's lesson. Both methods have structure. The first is uncreative and nonindividualistic. The second is better, even though every child in the class works on the same words. The secret lies in the source of those words. Thus the element of pupil choice can be seen as that practice which helps a child see what he needs to know when he needs to know it.

Where does a teacher start? Certainly one of the first decisions that must be made is what area of the curriculum, or what part of the school day, will lend itself most easily to individualization. If the schedule includes an independent work period, this seems a plausible place to start. Instead of requiring all children to do the same thing, a teacher can give each child an opportunity to choose what he will do. At first she can give him two alternatives rather than offering a bewildering array of possibilities.

As a teacher feels more and more secure, he is likely to set up more and more independent activities until, *mirabile dictu*, eventually pupils reach that state of grace where they develop their own projects with only teacher assistance, not teacher direction. In short, individuality can be expanded from a double choice, to a triple choice, to a multiple choice, to finally the most open-ended activities.

Another point the teacher moving toward increased individualizing must consider is the effect of these activities upon scheduling and planning. The lockstep of rigid schedules, those posted on doors of classrooms, can kill incentive.

I know teachers that begin each school day with a twenty- to thirty-minute period, during which every child accounts individually for his plans for the day. This does not mean that activities involving the whole class are excluded, but it does mean that each child develops his own projects based on some part of a curriculum area. Maybe he is learning cursive writing. During independent work time, he assigns himself the practicing of letters that bother him the most. The teacher may help or not, but he is on call and has an eye out for those who need him.

Individualization is possible when a teacher is convinced that children will work hard if they have some choice in what they are to do. The idea that an activity is valuable only if it is unpleasant or difficult must be thrown away. Children are dynamos of energy when what they are doing is important to them. This is not pampering, or coddling, or even laissez-faire. It is exciting education.

OPEN-ENDED ACTIVITIES

The kind of individualization we want to discuss comes about through open-ended activities. Such activities enable the teacher to see when to group, when to have one-to-one conferences, and when to work with the whole class at the same time. Here are some examples:

Math. Cuisenaire rods are well known as manipulative devices. While they are particularly suitable for the lower grades, children at any level can play with them. Extremely limited children, such as the brain-damaged, can use them for self-entertainment. And perhaps in the same classroom, a gifted child can take the rods and move into advanced mathematical calculations. Thus a teacher watching pupils work (each by himself but in company with others) at their own levels of simplicity or complexity has a way of assessing, of analyzing, or diagnosing, if you please, what each child needs to learn to improve his mathematical ability. She then arranges to teach as a group all those who have the same needs.

Mechanics of Written Language. Independent writing can serve a diagnostic purpose. Every pupil should do some creative writing each day—perhaps a journal or diary or his views on local or world events. Assessing such compositions, not necessarily correcting them, gives the teacher tangible evidence as to which mechanics of writing need to be taught to which children. Some pupils have trouble making tall letters. Others have no idea about punctuation. Many make certain types of spelling errors, have trouble with vowels, or find syllabication confusing. Those having the same problem can be taught as a group. Individuals having unique problems can be helped singly.

Spelling. To find out how far along in word analysis each child is, a teacher tests for auditory discrimination. While best done on a one-to-one basis, such testing can take place with a group or an entire class. "What letter begins this word?" the teachers ask. "Listen carefully." Then she pronounces a word she has thoughtfully selected and follows with others. Children can be tested in such a way on beginning sounds, ending sounds, and middle sounds of words. This clearly diagnostic activity shows the teacher *exactly* which child knows which sound. Once this knowledge is obtained and charted, the teacher knows what must be taught.

Reading. Individualized reading is better known to some teachers than other forms of individualization. The procedure is for all children to read individually from self-chosen books. Afterward, each child has frequently scheduled conferences with his teacher regarding the book. What needs to be done next is apparent to the teacher at each conference.

Music. A music teacher who wants to begin two-part singing starts the whole class singing in unison a song with simple harmony. "Down in the Valley" might be such a one. As all the children sing the melody, the teacher goes from child to child singing the *harmony* in each one's ear. Some children will simply sing the melody more loudly. Others will drop right into the harmony. Immediately the teacher knows how to divide the class so that he can teach two-part singing.

To Summarize. These activities are open-ended as to *time*. Lunch period does not really interrupt the analysis; it can go on later.

Open-endedness also applies to the *speed* at which a child works. The teacher can discover what he needs to learn whether the child goes fast or slow.

Finally, the activities are open-ended in respect to *ability*. Individualization ensures maximum activity for all ability levels —from the best reader to the worst—from the easiest talker to the most inarticulate—from the prolific author to the agonizingly slow low-verbal child.

The teacher who works out analyses from these open-ended procedures knows what needs to be taught. She may not always know *how* to teach it, but that is another story. Evidence has been gathered. Materials can now be organized to fit children, rather than the other way around. Through such approaches, the decades-old dream of a *child-centered class-room* is possible. The current term is *individualizing;* it means the same thing.

TEACHER-PUPIL CONFERENCE

Two major questions help teachers understand the how, when, and why of individualization. These are:

1. *When does a teacher teach directly?*
2. *When does a teacher set a situation and let learning happen?*

Instruction.   There are times, it seems to me, when a teacher must *instruct*. There are uncountable items in various areas that children will never figure out for themselves even though the habit of wanting to know, of being curious, of asking questions has been highly developed. At any school level, there has to be a place for expert knowledge. The teacher can be the expert or find someone who is.

Diagnostic operations help those who would tee off direct "learnin'." Thus such a teacher finds out what a child does not know, and teaches *that*, regardless of whether children are working singly, in groups, or in whole classes.

Ground Rules for Conferences.   Individual conferences, of course, are the best way to meet individual differences, but a teacher can waste valuable classroom time unless she makes a few rules and observes them.

1. Confer on a sample of a child's total work in a given area. You do not need to see everything each child does. Assume that a good job done on this sample will find the rest of the work at approximately the same level.

2. Let the sample be in some way the child's choice, for then he is personally committed to the learning. What the child brings may reveal an area of need you will recognize if he does not.

3. Work on types of problems or needs. What a child believes he needs may be a sign pointing out a greater need. As you consider a specific question or problem, think what type of learning is indicated.

4. Keep conferences open-ended. The fairest arrangement isn't necessarily to give every child the same amount of time. One child may always need more of your time than another. The same child will need more time on one occasion than on another. If open-endedness is achieved, the bright child will not be doing more than he needs to do in a given area and the slow child will not keep trying to catch up with much brighter ones.

5. Let the child feel your personal interest. Exciting teaching and genuine learning can never come through materials alone.

Special Curriculum Areas. Individual conferences may be held in respect to any area of the curriculum. But a conference is most easily set up after children have been exploring a vast array of material. For example:

In *arithmetic*, a teacher should know what to do next with individual children after watching them count or manipulate or, as I saw recently in an English educational film,[1] follow directions on "Order Cards."

In *written composition*, a child chooses, once a week or so, a piece of written material (uncorrected!) from the weeks' accumulation to bring to his teacher. He may recognize his

[1] *I Do and I Understand* (Nuffield Foundation of Modern Mathematics, Sound Service, Ltd., Wilton Crescent, Merton Park, S.W. 19, England).

general need to improve his composition or he may ask specific information related to spelling or punctuation.[2]

In *reading*, the child discusses a portion of a book he helped select and has been reading silently.[3]

Bridgeheads.   In closing this series on individualizing, it seems best to list some bridgeheads that apply to this most crucial teaching operation, regardless of curriculum area. There seem to be four of these.

1. Ask one or more questions that bring a response to the overall, general learning under discussion. In *reading*, questions will probe for central thought and inference. In *writing*, something about the scope or extent of the idea underlying the composition should be asked. In *arithmetic*, the questions will explore the meaning of numbers at whatever level the child reveals. In *social studies*, a question leading back to the problem statement of the unit helps.

2. Find out why this particular matter which he has brought to the conference especially interests the individual. "Why did you pick this for our conference?"

3. Explore the mechanics of learning as it pertains to the area under discussion. ("How did you get this or that? How do you think you can find out——?" "How did you get out of trouble when you were stuck?" "Where did you look for the answer?")

4. Give your conferee a chance to demonstrate a skill, display a piece of work, or perform an experiment. He has the

[2] For greater detail, see "Mechanics in Written English," by Alvina Treut Burrows, an article in the March 1962 issue of *The Instructor*, and "Functional Spelling," by the same author in *Individualizing Education* (Association for Childhood Education International, 3615 Wisconsin Ave., N.W., Washington, D.C. 20016; $1.25).

[3] The reader is directed to an excellent interim report by Lakeshore Curriculum Study Council, 2114 E. Kenwood Blvd., Milwaukee, Wis. 53211: "Three-Year Longitudinal Study Comparing Individualized and Basal Reading Programs at the Primary Level."

right to a place in the sun of teacher recognition. Sensible handling will not produce a braggart.

Finally. Individualization is not a method. It is a way to manage a classroom so that each child has his share of the teacher. Teaching is a human act. It fades when it is dehumanized. Children whose individual differences are truly met will be better taught—because of these differences and not in spite of them.

INDIVIDUALIZING INSTRUCTION

Bernice J. Wolfson

Consider these classroom activities:

The teacher reads a story to the class.

The children work at their seats on different workbook pages, story writing, or projects.

Four girls arrange a bulletin-board display.

Two boys share the same book.

Five pupils listen to a tape-recorded story.

Twenty pupils listen to a report about the school store.

Are these manifestations of individualized instruction? Perhaps yes, perhaps no. I observed all these activities in a classroom organized for this kind of instruction, but they could have taken place in a classroom that was not actually responsive to individual needs and interests. Indeed, even a one-to-one relationship does not necessarily meet individual needs, for a teacher can direct an individual conference exactly as she conducts work with the group.

Clearly, individualizing instruction does not mean primarily a tutorial arrangement, though a one-to-one relationship is, of course, included. Nor, I think, does it encompass subgrouping on a permanent or semipermanent basis.

Whether at the elementary or secondary level, groups should be formed on the basis of a common interest, learning problem, or special task and be disbanded as soon as their purpose is accomplished. Some things, such as planning for shared activities and offering suggestions for solving a general prob-

Reprinted from *NEA Journal*, Vol. 55, November 1966, pp. 31–33, with permission of the author and publisher.

lem, are more reasonably done in groups (sometimes small, sometimes large) than by individuals.

A crucial concept which separates individualized from group instruction is the rejection of the idea that all learners must move through a predetermined, sequenced curriculum. Merely permitting different rates of speed will not provide for individual differences. Essentially, individualizing instruction requires the teacher to encourage individual interests, allow for individual styles, and respond to individual needs.

Two basic facts support the need to individualize instruction. First, as any classroom teacher knows, students vary tremendously. Not only do they differ in shape, size, energy level, and other physical characteristics but also in rate of development, temperament, motivation, previous experience, and style of learning. Second, the human being is an active, seeking organism that does more than merely react to his environment; he also explores and changes it.

Furthermore, the purposes of education, at least as I see them, support the need to individualize instruction. One of these is the development of individuality. The press for conformity is strong in our culture, and certainly some conformity is essential for living in any society. We are not faced, however, with choosing individuality *or* conformity but rather with the issue of balance and meaning.

Other purposes of the school include promoting an understanding of the world and encouraging each child's self-fulfillment and competency. In order to develop individuality and feelings of competence and to move toward self-actualization, children need to learn how to learn, to think independently, to make choices, to plan, and to evaluate.

The history of education is replete with accounts of efforts by sensitive teachers and administrators to cope with the great range of individual differences. Approaches have included individual projects, tutoring on a one-to-one basis, programed learning, and a variety of organizational plans (for example, cross-grade grouping, continuous progress, nongraded classrooms, and multi-age classes). None of these guarantees individualization of instruction. Organization and materials can only provide the environment and arrangements which free a teacher to meet the educational needs of all the pupils in the class.

What a teacher *is* and *does* remains the crucial variable in the classroom. Inevitably one needs to ask: What is the teacher doing in the classroom? What assumptions does he make about the nature of children and how they learn? What attitudes and expectations does he communicate to the class?

Even those who agree on the need to individualize instruction may have different operational approaches based on conflicting sets of assumptions.

One approach views the teacher as a diagnostician who, with the aid of various tests, subject matter specialists, and consultants, determines what each student should learn. He then prescribes and assigns appropriate tasks and materials. In some cases, the teacher may bypass much of this operation and allow programs, textbooks, and curriculum guides to take over. But, essentially, the teacher is still making the decisions and carrying out the program.

Another approach assumes that real individualization of instruction, in ways that are meaningful to the learner, requires a good deal of self-selection and self-direction by the learner. The teacher in this operation is primarily a consultant to the learner and a manager of the classroom environment. His role is to help students learn to plan and evaluate, to provide stimulating experiences, to make students aware of many alternatives when making decisions, to supply a variety of appropriate materials.

He responds both to the requests of individuals and to his own hypotheses as to what variety of materials and opportunities might be helpful.

Reflection on the two approaches described above should make it clear that nongraded schools may represent the first or the second kind of operation. Most nongraded schools, as they exist today, are in fact graded by reading achievement. Children are grouped for "likenesses" and put through essentially the same curriculum. By contrast, a nongraded class which is multi-age and heterogeneous may be viewed as composed of thirty unique individuals who, from time to time, have common interests and needs.

Programed learning, as developed to date, is mostly related to allowing for different *rates* of learning. It is the manner in which programs are used in the classroom that determines whether or not they facilitate individualization. Self-selected, relatively short units of work would support individualization; long units required of all pupils would not.

Many of the current innovations and restorations (such as programed learning, special grouping, nongraded organization, and team teaching) allow for minor adaptations to individual differences but rest on the old assumption that there exists a graded body of skills and content which is most appropriately learned in a preplanned sequence. This assumption definitely impedes efforts to individualize instruction.

Another impediment is the fact that parents, teachers, administrators, and even children are inclined to define success and failure in terms of graded expectations. A child who is learning and increasing his competency is often labeled as failing because he hasn't succeeded in the arbitrary sequence set up for all learners in a particular grade.

The alternative to trying to patch up a system which rests on values and assumptions contradictory to those which are behind individualized approaches is to reconceptualize both the organization and the content of schooling. Let me say, without going into detail, that I believe the following assumptions are important in working toward the long-term educational goals basic to individualized instruction.

1. For real learning to occur, the learner must see a purpose and meaning in the learning experience.
2. No *best* method exists for all teachers to use in teaching anything to all children.
3. The way a teacher interacts with children affects the amount they learn, their feelings about learning, and their feelings about themselves.
4. There is no best structure in the disciplines nor a best sequence in skill development.

Classroom procedures and organizations which I think are appropriate include:

1. Grouping for diversity (multi-age, nongraded) with opportunities for *temporary* subgroups to pursue special interests and competencies
2. Self-selection in reading and in interest groups from many alternatives (This requires a wide range of human, material, and audio-visual resources.)
3. Opportunities for independent work, alone and in small groups
4. Individual and small-group conferences with the teacher for pupil-teacher planning and evaluation and for teacher assistance as needed

In the final analysis, the classroom teacher (supported by administrators and parents) must translate his own values and goals into action.

As far as traditional school content is concerned, during the primary years I would emphasize exploratory activities in the various content areas as well as the development of skills in communication, learning, and human relations. In the intermediate years (with overlap into both primary and upper levels), I would provide opportunities for selecting more systematic approaches to developed knowledge alternating with exploratory activities and discussions of personal meanings.

Today's problem of meeting individual needs and providing for individual differences in our mass education system is extremely difficult to resolve. Although educators may agree on the need to effect changes in this direction, we sorely need to work out some philosophically consistent practices which will develop and support individuality.

TEACHING FOR INDIVIDUALITY AND PERSONAL LEARNING

Bernice J. Wolfson

Since I first wrote about individualizing instruction in 1962, I have been struggling, somewhat unsatisfactorily, with the ambiguous meanings of this concept. In that first paper I simply avoided defining it. I said that individualization of instruction "refers to ways teachers find of continuing to develop the uniqueness of each child." (1:457)[1] From this guideline, each teacher would have to develop her own definitions. Subsequently, I tried to describe how teachers and pupils behave when they are endeavoring to individualize instruction (2, 3, 4). Finally, last year I developed these roles in greater detail and also tried to clarify the meaning of individualized instruction by contrasting my interpretation with an opposing viewpoint (5). In the course of this development, I have discovered that I am not really talking about individualized instruction but rather about personal learning. And is that not a dead end? For what other kind of learning is there?

But, in the typical school setting, what we often call learning does not refer to the child's personal learning. As George

Address presented at a Workshop on Individualized Instruction, University of California, Los Angeles, June, 1968. Reprinted with permission of the author.

[1] Numbers in parentheses refer to references at end of chapter.

Dennison (6) suggested, many children in school are unaware of *whole forms* of learning. What they have seen defined as learning is "remembering, reciting, copying, answering questions, taking tests—and these, alas, do not add up to learning." (6:153) The personal learning that actually goes on in most classrooms, where self-directed personal learning is not part of the legitimate school activity, has been described by Dennison as "self-defense against the environment." (6:153) Self-defense may take the form of withdrawing from involvement, of rebelling against the system, or of adapting to the expectations of the system. Most children learn to conform, to figure out the teacher, to relate to their peers in a restrictive setting, and in general to beat the system. At the same time other kinds of personal learning are part of their out-of-school life. I am reminded of one high school student whose teachers had no idea of the advanced level and large quantity of books he was reading at home, nor of the experiments with rats he was carrying out in his basement.

In educational circles much of what goes on in school is justified or attacked on the basis of "what we know about learning." Certainly before we can talk about instruction we have to know what assumptions we are making about how children learn. Particularly, we need to know what we are expecting children to do under different conceptions of instruction. I shall describe only two models of teaching-learning which may be viewed as the extremes of a wide range of possibilities involving more or less predetermined structure. These models are programed learning and self-directed personal learning. Under these two plans for instruction, what is the student doing?

PROCESS IN PROGRAMED LEARNING

We can describe a programed learning situation as consisting of a planned sequence of activities with some possibility for modification by the learner. Someone has set up a logical organization and sequence for some predetermined content. This sequence may include some alternative sub-sequences. Let us imagine ourselves as students; we need simply to get on the track and continue through this preplanned program to its destination. However we could drop out in the middle of the program instead of working through to the end. Our first task in this situation might be to choose a program. It is more likely that the teacher would choose it for us or even the central office. Other tasks we would engage in are reading the information provided and answering the questions asked. If we found sections that weren't clear to us, we might reread them and try to figure them out or we might ask someone to help us. We might find it helpful to turn back a few pages, but probably not to skip any. If the program were carefully prepared and pretested, it is likely that we would move along easily though some of us might possibly become bored. In any case, we will have "learned" whatever the content was when we have read the statements, worked the problems, and answered the questions. This content might concern information or process. For example, a program about the origin of the slide rule would be informational, while one about how to use a slide rule would be procedural.

Research on programed learning suggests that some students will arrive at the criterion results for the program more rapidly than others, with a net saving of time when compared to a situation in which a teacher is trying to teach the same content to a group or class. As far as I know, the studies comparing programed learning with other procedures in terms of retention or transfer, rather than just saving time, have not led to clear-cut findings. The main difficulties with research in this field are: a lack of clearly defined comparative models (compared to what?) and the questionable adequacy of the criterion measures. It should be noted, of course, that these same difficulties exist in practically all educational research.

When we reflect upon programed learning, we must ask also what is the student learning about the process of learning. What does he find out about how to learn as he progresses within this model? We also need to know how different students respond to this way of learning and whether some kinds of content are more appropriately learned this way than others. These are some of the basic questions about which users of programed learning materials need information. Even hunches derived from experience with these materials would be useful to teachers at the present stage of program development.

It may be argued that the programed learning model makes sense for learning certain relatively closed systems, for example, some areas of mathematics or science, while the personal learning model is suited to learning in the humanities and the arts and possibly other aspects of mathematics and science. Perhaps we need also to consider that different students might respond best to one or the other of these two models and might not be equally able to learn both ways. Conceivably individual programs may be selected as a part of self-directed personal learning. It is hard to envision the opposite situation, that is, self-directed personal learning as part of programed instruction. It seems to be a contradiction of terms. Note, however, Mager's (7) work with learner-directed programs.

I must admit I have doubts about what, in fact, is learned through programs or teaching machines in their present form. One can circle correct answers and supply correct words or phrases but still have no personal connections with this "knowledge." Consider, for example, the difference between a map and the terrain it represents. It is possible to know a lot about maps but obtain (or should I say create) little meaning from the map because one has had no experience with the actual phenomena in their natural, complex forms.

PROCESS IN SELF-DIRECTED LEARNING

Let us turn now to how we might behave as learners in the second model. What tasks are required by a model of self-directed personal learning? We might start a particular learning sequence by choosing a question. For example, how did this particular street in this town, which has the same name as a boy in our class, get this name? Or, we might begin by selecting a topic of interest such as "color." Or, we might select a broader area of interest such as archaeology. Since sequence is flexible and overlapping, our choice could be preceded or followed by some general exploratory activity in the form of reading, discussion, or viewing a film. We might prefer to begin by considering what we think we know, or what we are curious about. At various points we would search for resources in the form of books, films or filmstrips, magazines, places, or people. We would choose which resources to use and how long to pursue our activity. Our decision would be based on a variety of criteria. For example, I might stay with one topic as long as I care about it or as long as I find it exciting or aesthetically pleasing. Most of our tasks as learners in this model consist of searching, developing and assessing alternatives, making a variety of decisions, carrying out a plan, and evaluating our progress.

I am not aware of any research that deals with this model of learning. Some relevant studies have been done which compare individualized instruction in reading to a variety of other approaches. Findings, as in most educational research, are unclear. However, there is a trend showing more positive attitudes toward reading with an individualized approach.

RESEARCH AND CLASSROOM LEARNING

To the present time most educational research has not dealt with the kind of questions relevant to self-directed personal learnings. (8) A brief summary of the kinds of research most frequent in education will bear this out. Also, because the classroom situation is so complex, investigators of teaching and learning have usually selected some segment or element of the total system. The segment selected for study and the findings which result depend on the kinds of questions of interest to the researcher. The most common questions studied are not concerned with personal learning.

Questions about the impact of the school on children's learning have led to the examination of certain kinds of evidence. Typically, these include achievement tests, attitude inventories, and some measures of self-concept. Certain interview techniques may be used to find out the child's perception of his learning experience. Whatever measures may be used to answer questions about where children are at some point in time, it is often not clear what factors in the complex classroom situation contributed to the results. Even more seriously, we have little idea about the significance of the variable we are measuring in the child's total learning experience.

Questions about what actually happens in classrooms have led to a variety of studies in classroom settings. The Observation Schedule developed by Medley and Mitzel (9:275) was designed to systematically record the total situation in the classroom. Anderson's (10) study of integrative and dominative teachers, and Kounin's (11) studies of classroom discipline are examples of selected types of classroom analysis. Jackson (12) studied life in classrooms and also interviewed teachers to analyze their concepts of teaching.

Studies by Hughes (13), Flanders (14), Smith (15), and Bellack (16) among others have focused on oral communication in the classroom situation. From their studies we can learn whether the discourse of teachers is logical, how teachers control the dialogue with their students, and how teachers respond to children along certain specified dimensions. We can also note how teachers differ from each other in their oral communication. The results of these investigations have been clearly described but are only tangential to questions about student learning in the classroom. Moreover, many are concerned with a very limited aspect of school experience, teacher-class discussion.

Another kind of question frequently asked in educational research is whether one organization, method, approach, or set of materials is better than others. This has led to a host of studies about class grouping, individualized reading, programed learning, ITA, and various new curriculum packages. It seems highly unlikely that one approach to instruction or one set of materials will prove superior for all children or under all conditions.

In all this research there are no efforts which focus primarily on questions relevant to self-directed personal learning. I doubt if I know what the appropriate questions are, but I would tentatively suggest that we are interested in such dimensions as the learner's awareness of alternatives, his commitment to learning, his understanding of himself and others, and the ways he has of coping with new situations. We are also interested in his continuous growth in the basic processes necessary to be a self-directed learner, viz., (a) reading and using reading, (b) thinking quantitatively, (c) communicating orally and in writing, and (d) planning and evaluating his progress. In addition we might explore what kind of instructional role is appropriate with this model of learning.

Educational research which focuses on what the teacher plans or what she thinks she is doing is extremely rare (17). No doubt the relationship is far from clear, but there must be some connection between what the teacher thinks and how she works with children in the classroom. Studies dealing with teacher personality and classroom results have not been very informative. Instead of the teacher's personality, we might study the teacher's deliberations. How does a teacher plan to encourage self-directed personal learning? What values does she hold? On what bases does she make decisions?

PROCESS IN TEACHING

As a teacher I have some general image of the kind of teacher I am or would like to be. This image is interrelated with my values and attitudes. As a result, I believe I encourage students to make their own decisions, I ask for their real concerns and interests, and I listen carefully to them. From my frame of reference, a neat paper does not take precedence over a neat idea. Learning about geography is not more important than learning about modern art. Whatever I value must certainly interact with my plans as I think about what can be done in the classroom.

Of course, a teacher engages in both reflective and spontaneous behavior. Reflecting on school events in the evening, or before school starts in the morning, is an inevitable part of being a teacher. Whether she puzzles about John's temper tantrum yesterday or about what materials Jane's group will need today, these reflections lead to some actions she will take in the classroom. She is also engaged in spontaneous behavior in the classroom. There are a million decisions to be made which do not allow for reflection. For example, should she intervene now or would it be better for Jimmy to work out the problem by himself? How will she decide between two simultaneous demands for her assistance? Many of these decisions are not reflected upon, but I think they are related to her previous reflections, to her values, and to her feelings and attitudes. All these are part of the total context of the interaction.

This description suggests to me that many factors operate which we cannot yet spell out or define. Perhaps some factors we will never clearly understand. We may refer for example to concepts such as intuition or the preconscious (18) or "tacit knowledge." (19) Whatever concepts we use to talk about this phenomenon, they point to the existence of feelings and knowledge of which we are not focally aware at a particular time. This is not an antiscientific or magical view. In fact, most descriptions of scientific discovery, of the work of artists and writers, and of the variation among human beings in terms of awareness and sensitivity deal with various aspects of this phenomenon.

I don't believe we will ever understand what goes on between teachers and pupils if we ignore this subrational reality and insist on purely rational systems. The most common rational system which has been urged on teachers for many years is the use of behavioral objectives as a basis for planning, carrying out, and evaluating instruction. I do not believe it is a realistic system.

TEACHING FOR INDIVIDUALITY

How could a teacher plan to move toward more individualization of instruction or, as I would rather describe it, toward providing conditions for more personal learning in the classroom? I think she needs first to focus on her beliefs and values to determine if they are consistent with such a move. Does she believe pupils can and should make decisions about their own learning? Is she willing to let them do so? (There are other values and beliefs she needs to examine. This is just one example.) In my opinion the conditions that a teacher would provide to support individuality and personal learning include: increasing the amount of pupil planning in the classroom, both individually and in small groups; providing children more opportunities to make decisions; and having a wide variety of materials and resources available. The teacher would also give greater consideration to the interests and concerns of her pupils. A further direction I think important is to pay more attention to process. By this I mean raising questions with the class or individual students such as: How shall we go about it? What do you think you will need? What do you want me to do? Who needs help? Who will give it? and so on.

How any teacher, any particular teacher, might initiate changes in the direction of self-directed, personal learning is hard to say. Eventually, each teacher has to decide on ways that make sense to her. Sometimes, a teacher might start by making self-selection of reading materials possible in a reading group and gradually allowing this procedure to spread to other groups; and then to spread to other areas of the curriculum. Or, she might encourage a group of volunteers to pursue some interest that has emerged by chance and work with them to help them get started. Another teacher might sit down with the whole class to plan. They would discuss how they were going to go about using their time (perhaps for an afternoon), and individuals or groups would choose areas of interest to work in.

Or a teacher might start with areas for which so-called homogeneity and gradedness are clearly irrelevant. The language arts area in particular has many opportunities for activities of this kind: sharing one's favorite stories or acting out a story, planning and preparing a class newspaper or magazine, writing and then sharing an original story—all of these activities (and any true learning for that matter) have no real relationship to the notions of gradedness or homogeneity with which we have so persistently organized our schools. Probably any area of study in which a teacher is particularly comfortable would be a good place for her to start moving toward providing opportunities for self-directed, personal learning.

Another kind of change which would enable a teacher to move in the direction we are discussing is to try to break down the time structure. A period of independent work time, during which children can read or do arithmetic or pursue interest group activities, eliminates the notion that there is a time when everyone has to be engaged in reading or when everyone has to be doing arithmetic. Breaking down the time structure will also lead to some changes in classroom grouping which I shall describe later.

I believe that it is also necessary to stop thinking in the usual subject-matter categories and to reject the belief that a pre-determined sequence is necessary. This change allows the real questions of children about the world around them to come into the classroom. It also allows children to move out into the world instead of being isolated in the classroom. The special interests of the teacher can also be welcomed. In addition to encouraging individuality and the pursuit of self-directed learning on the part of children, this particular change will provide opportunities for including areas of study and approaches to knowledge that have been kept out of the classroom by the constraints of subject matter and curriculum guides. In most classrooms today, it would be difficult to find time to discuss some aspects of anthropology, archaeology, or sociology not to mention poverty, violence, or understanding people. By providing opportunities for the pursuit of the interests of children and teacher, it is possible to broaden the scope of classroom content.

The teacher can also encourage the use of a variety of human resources by her students: parents, older children, and other teachers. Wherever there is someone with special interests, special knowledge, and particularly with special enthusiasm, that person is a valuable resource for learning.

The new classroom organization can include a variety of kinds of grouping but not achievement or ability grouping on the basis of test scores. While there would certainly be individual conferences with the teacher, there would also be small group conferences. At times the whole class would get together for planning, but small groups could plan with the teacher as needed and certainly individuals would. Most teachers have found it useful to schedule an independent work time in the morning and afternoon. Plans should be flexible so this time would vary in length according to class needs. At various points in the day there might be a sharing time or time when the class gathers together to help some group with problems they have had in pursuing their inquiry. At times the class might want to hold meetings to discuss various procedural or organizational matters which concern the entire group. From day to day, the class schedule would vary. I do not believe that children are upset by this variation particularly if they are involved to a large extent in the planning and if the decisions that are reached are placed where anyone can refer to them. The day's plan could be written on the blackboard or distributed on a ditto sheet prepared by a planning committee.

I have worked with a number of teachers who have been trying to move in the direction I have been describing. Although to some extent these changes can be carried out in any class, I have been particularly interested in working with teachers who have multiage, heterogeneous classes. This type of grouping, I believe, supports an individualized, personalized approach to teaching and learning.

PROBLEMS OF CHANGE

In working with these teachers, I have emphasized the importance of pupil planning and of organizing interest groups. I asked the teachers, as we worked together, to describe some of the problems they met and some of the concerns they had about how their classes were operating. Probably the most frequent concern was the problem of getting an adequate amount and variety of materials in the interest areas that the children selected and at appropriate levels of difficulty. This problem of variety of materials at different levels was also frequently raised in the area of mathematics.

A number of teachers expressed concern about whether they were still making too many decisions for the children and not really encouraging them to be more autonomous in their learning. Also many of them worried about whether their beginning readers were making enough progress. (This is a very interesting persistent problem related, I believe, to the presures in our society and in the establishment to have children begin to read as soon as possible if not sooner.)

Another concern the teachers expressed was their own anxiety when they saw children who didn't happen to be busy at the moment. How much of this, they ask, is acceptable and how much is too much? An additional concern that came up was how to help children work well together. As one teacher expressed it, when the children were working in groups, some of them were rather bossy. But, of course, problems of inter-personal relations exist in every classroom. For the most part, it has seemed to us that multi-age classroom organization encouraged children to work more helpfully together. In summary, teachers' comments about their classroom problems have focused on the need for additional help in getting resources into the classroom and on some of their own problems in thinking about how they see themselves as teachers, what they expect children to learn, and how they expect children to behave in their classroom.

Another problem that our teachers were concerned about was the reaction of other teachers who were not engaged in the multi-age program. They felt that these teachers were re-acting unfavorably to what was going on in the innovative classrooms. They also felt, at least in some of the schools I worked with, that the principal was not sufficiently suppor-tive and at times didn't seem to understand what they were trying to do.

If teachers are to be encouraged to change, they need to be encouraged to develop their own individuality and indepen-dence and for this they need adequate support—support that allows them time to reflect about what they're doing and dis-cuss it, support that provides a greater backing up of teachers' work by helping them to obtain the resources they need in the classroom.

The minimum essential a teacher requires in order to change is the support of her principal and another teacher in the build-ing who will join in her efforts. Individual parents often pro-vide considerable support for teachers. Even though some of the teachers with whom I have worked have had a minimum of additional support, they have found that the changes they made resulted in more interesting and satisfying classroom experiences for both themselves and their students.

The changes I have suggested mean that the adult in the classroom is not and should not simply be a "teacher" in the old sense of the word. Rather, she is an alive and growing person who spends her time in the company of other alive and growing persons called children. The teacher, like the child, should experience self-directed, personal learning as she copes with the still unsolved problem of how to help others learn.

References

1. WOLFSON, BERNICE J., "The Educational Scene." *Elementary English*, Vol. 40 (April 1963), 456–560.

2. ———, "Individualization of Instruction." *The Journal of the Reading Specialist*, Vol. 5 (December 1965), 45–53.

3. ———, "Individualizing Instruction." *NEA Journal*, Vol. 55 (November 1966), 31–33.

4. ———, "The Promise of Multiage Grouping for Individualizing Instruction." *The Elementary School Journal*, Vol. 67 (April 1967), 354–362.

5. ———, "Teacher and Pupil Roles in Individualized Instruction." *The Elementary School Journal*, Vol. 68 (April 1968), 357–366.

6. DENNISON, GEORGE, "The First Street School." *New American Review*, No. 3 (April 1968), 150–171.

7. MAGER, ROBERT F., AND C. CLARK, "Explorations in Student-Controlled Instruction." *Psychological Reports*, Vol. 13 (August 1963), 71–76.

8. Numerous studies are reported in the following books:

   a. BELLACK, ARNO A. (ED.), *Theory and Research in Teaching.* New York: Teachers College, Columbia University, 1963.

   b. BIDDLE, BRUCE J., AND WILLIAM J. ELLENA (EDS.), *Contemporary Research on Teacher Effectiveness.* New York: Holt, Rinehart and Winston, 1964.

   c. GAGE, N. L. (ED.), *Handbook of Research on Teaching.* Chicago: Rand McNally & Company, 1963.

9. MEDLEY, DONALD M., AND HAROLD E. MITZEL, "Measuring Classroom Behavior by Systematic Observation," in N. L. Gage (Ed.)

Handbook of Research on Teaching. Chicago: Rand McNally & Company, 1963, pp. 247–328.

10. ANDERSON, HAROLD H., AND HELEN M. BREWER, "Studies of Teachers' Classroom Personalities. I. Dominative and Socially Integrative Behavior of Kindergarten Teachers." *Applied Psychology Monographs*, No. 6, 1945, also in No. 8 and 11. See also N. L. Gage (8.c.), Chapters 6 and 13.

11. KOUNIN, JACOB S., AND P. V. GUMP, "The Ripple Effect in Discipline." *Elementary School Journal*, Vol. 59 (December 1958) 158–162. See also N. L. Gage, Chapter 13.

12. JACKSON, PHILIP W., *Life in Classrooms*. New York: Holt, Rinehart and Winston, 1968.

13. HUGHES, MARIE, AND ASSOCIATES, *The Assessment of the Quality of Teaching: A Research Report*. U.S. Office of Education Cooperative Research Project, No. 353, Salt Lake City, University of Utah, 1959. See also N. L. Gage, Chapter 6, and A. Bellack (8.a.).

14. FLANDERS, NED A., *Teacher Influence, Pupil Attitudes, and Achievement: Studies in Interaction Analysis*. U.S. Office of Education Cooperative Research Project, No. 397, Minneapolis: University of Minnesota, 1960. See also N. L. Gage (Ed.), Chapter 6, and A. Bellack (8.a.).

15. SMITH, B. OTHANEL, AND ASSOCIATES, *A Study of the Logic of Teaching*. U.S. Office of Education Cooperative Research Project, No. 258 (7257), Urbana: University of Illinois, 1960. See also N. L. Gage.

16. BELLACK, ARNO A., AND ASSOCIATES, *The Language of the Classroom*. New York: Teachers College, Columbia University, 1966.

17. a. JACKSON, PHILIP W., AND ELIZABETH BELFORD, "Educational Objectives and the Joys of Teaching." *The School Review*, Vol. 73 (Autum 1965), 267–291.

    b. ———, "Private Affairs in Public Settings, Observations on Teaching in Elementary Schools." *The School Review*, Vol. 75 (Summer 1967), 172–186.

18. KUBIC, LAWRENCE, "Research in Protecting Preconscious Functions in Education," in Richard M. Jones (Ed.) *Contemporary Educational Psychology Selected Essays*. New York: Harper & Row, 1966, pp. 12–88.

19. POLANY, MICHAEL, *The Tacit Dimension*. Garden City, N. Y.: Doubleday & Co., 1966.

WHEN THE TEACHER DIAGNOSES LEARNING

Madeline Hunter

What kind of a boy is Johnny? What has he already learned? What "next" learning tasks are appropriate for him? How can a teacher increase the efficiency and economy of his accomplishment?

As the teacher confronts these questions for each learner under his supervision, small wonder he is tempted to murmur, "Please pass the crystal ball!" Fortunately, crystal balls and divining rods are not available on supply requisition lists, so professional rigor is beginning to replace folklore and fantasy as the basis for diagnosis of and for educational prespcription for the learner.

This shift from routinized application of the currently recommended panacea (what is it this year, look-say or phonics?) to decision making based on critical evaluation of each learner has been the major factor in the change from the technology of teaching to the profession of education.

No longer is diagnosis restricted to or reserved for only the educationally "sick." Rather, such diagnosis has become an intrinsic part of the teaching act for *all* learners. Out of such diagnosis are created educational prescriptions. The repertoire of competencies of the teacher and alternatives offered by the school constitute a pharmacy from which such prescriptions are filled.

From *Educational Leadership*, Volume 23, April, 1966, pp. 545–549. Reprinted with permission of the Association for Supervision and Curriculum Development and Madeline Hunter. Copyright (©) 1966 by the Association for Supervision and Curriculum Development.

We first must identify the questions such diagnosis is designed to answer. Only then can we seek instruments whose validity, reliability, and precision give us confidence in the accuracy of the assessment on which diagnosis is based.

DIAGNOSTIC QUESTIONS

Identification of the essential and relevant has as its irrefutable and logical counterpart identification of the nonessential and irrelevant. The latter, no matter how fascinating and tempting (with *that* home situation what can you expect of me?), must be discarded. We also must discard many of our most easily collected but relatively worthless "test results" on learners.

Each datum we use in our diagnostic procedure must pass the screen of contributing to the answer to one of the following questions:

1. What objective is appropriate for this learner to achieve? (Notice the change from "*I* am seeking to attain with this learner.")
2. What is his present status in relation to that objective?
3. What is the next learning step in attainment of that objective?
4. Based on data about this particular learner, what can the teacher do to help him take that step efficiently and economically?
5. Was he successful?
6. If so, what is the next appropriate step?
7. If not, what changes should be made?

Questions 1, 2, and 3 are content-based. Knowledge of the learning task (reading, math, or ball playing) must be related to the assessment of the learner's present degree of achievement.

Question 4 is learner-based. An assessment of the intellectual, physical, social, and emotional factors that contribute to or detract from the learning process provides the data for the answer.

Questions 5, 6, and 7 are evaluation-based, where "at this moment in time" must become the qualifying phrase for any answer.

Let us begin with an inspection of these questions as they relate to a physical activity so we will not get trapped in the value-imbued educational platitudes ("competency in reading," "appreciation of the democratic process"), which are so emotionally charged. Suppose we are trying to determine the appropriate high jump objective for a boy of a given age. The first factor that becomes obvious is that other data may be more critical than his age. Does he have long or short legs? Is he fat or thin? How well is he muscled and co-ordinated? (It makes you stop to reconsider the statement that ten-year-old boys should be reading at a fifth grade level, does it not?)

Suppose we agree that this boy should be able to clear a five-foot bar. Now we turn to our second question—how high can he actually jump? We find (possibly to our horror) that he can comfortably clear only a 3' 8" bar, although on occasions he can jump a 4' one. Obviously, at this point we are not going to insist he keep trying the 5' bar, but plan to start teaching so he can consistently clear the 4' one. (Hammering away at fifth grade work that is too difficult is as obviously unsound.)

Our fouth question is concerned with the use of data about the learner that will guide us in planning the learning opportunity and teaching strategy to help him accomplish his task. Will competition with other jumpers stimulate or retard his effort? What for him is the optimum ratio of success to failure? If he responds well to performance heavily weighted with success, we had better keep the bar at 3' 10". If he is motivated by the frustration of some failure, let us start at 4'. What does he need in the way of teacher support? Shall we stand by to encourage or let him work by himself? Does he respond well to his own perception of growth or does he need public recognition of his achievement? Will his parents contribute to his achievement motivation or do they think high jumping is a waste of time? (His parents may be getting a divorce or his father may be an alcoholic; however, these dramatic bits of information are not relevant unless we find evidence that they contribute to or detract from his accomplishment of the learning task.)

Now that we have defined the task, and applied a teaching strategy to help him accomplish it, did it work? If the answer is "yes," we are ready to move on to the next task, raise the height of the bar and proceed. If the answer is "no," we must look for factors that may need to be changed. Have we correctly assessed his jumping ability or should we have started with a lower bar? Could there be something wrong of which we were not aware (fatigue, low energy, movement or co-ordination difficulties)? Was our teaching strategy ineffective? Should we have given more encouragement? Should we have been "tougher" and insisted he "get at it" with consequences if he did not? Would making him the high-jump coach for less able jumpers do the trick? Are there other factors operating which we had not taken into consideration? By practicing, he may miss the opportunity to talk with fascinating girls or perhaps he may be attempting to insure our continued attention by his lack of success.

Our estimate of the correct answer to all of these diagnostic questions becomes the basis for an adjusted educational prescription. Again we fill the prescription from the pharmacy of teaching competency and the alternatives possible in the school and again assess its effectiveness by the performance of the jumper.

DIAGNOSIS IN READING

Let us now pose these same questions in the diagnosis of a learner we find in every classroom.

Bill is not performing well in reading. While not so remedial that he needs special help, he is dragging at the bottom of his group. We have the uncomfortable feeling that the only thing he is learning is that reading is a bore to be avoided whenever possible.

We begin our diagnosis with the first question, "What goal is appropriate for this learner?" Notice by using goal in the singular, we are being forced to give priority to "enjoyment of reading" *or* "skills in reading" *or* "appreciation of literature" *or* "more active participation in the reading program." Once we identify the primary goal we are able to deal with or eliminate the incompatibility of other goals. (Chaucer and enjoyment may not be compatible at this point. Unidentified, their counter-directions can neutralize our teaching efforts.

If we select "enjoyment of reading" as the goal basic to the achievement of all others, this becomes our criterion for answering subsequent questions. (It also eliminates such temptations as having his dad make him read an hour each night.)

Our second question, "What is his present status in relation to that goal?" involves a valid assessment of Bill. The eyes and ears of a well-prepared teacher continue to be among the best instruments of appraisal; however, we can validate or supplement these observations with objective tests. There is a relationship (but not one-to-one correspondence) between enjoyment of and skill in an activity, so we need carefully to assess Bill's reading skills. We look beyond the homogenized 5.3 grade placement score on the fact sheet of a reading test because the information we are seeking is inside the test and we will find it only if we inspect Bill's responses.

What kinds of items did he miss? Did he do the easy ones correctly and then quit? Were careless errors responsible for missing easy items while he passed harder ones? Could his errors indicate an attempt to respond correctly or was he simply filling in the blanks? Most important, how does his test performance compare with our daily perception of him? If he performs significantly better in either the test or classroom, what factors might be responsible? Obviously, a numerical grade placement score does not begin to answer these questions.

Let us assume our answer is: Bill *can* read fifth grade material with understanding but the vocabulary load slows him down. Fourth grade material insures a more comfortable pace; however, the content of both fourth and fifth grade material he finds uninteresting. When the reading is difficult he seems to turn off his effort and make wild guesses. When the content is uninteresting, he withdraws into daydreaming with a resultant lack of focus on the learning task.

Our assessment of Bill's performance should direct us to the answer to the question, "What is the next appropriate learning step?"

Now we have two criteria to guide us. The material must be easy enough to encourage his progress and interesting enough to hold his focus. This may involve abandoning, for a time, the state series and selecting a book with a low vocabulary load and exciting content. Remember, "enjoyment of reading" is the goal with highest priority at this point in time. (We are adjusting the high jump bar so he can get over it.) We have not abandoned word attack skills and extraction of meaning but we are concentrating on first things first.

Having selected an appropriate task, we now turn to our design to help him accomplish it. Here our diagnosis of the learner requires professional literacy in learning theory and personality theory. To what reward system will he respond? Will his accomplishment be positively reinforcing or do we need to add the social rewards of praise and recognition? Do we need to suppress any behavior (such as avoidance of reading) by negative reinforcement? Will *in*creasing or *de*creasing anxiety result in better motivation? How long a reading period can he tolerate before negative feelings take over? How might we extend this period?

These are samples of the questions we must answer for a valid diagnosis. The questions determine whether we skillfully entice him into the reading task or arbitrarily assign it with a time limit and consequences. We may make him the star performer in a book review or may quietly converse with him when the rest of the group are busy. We may make reading a definite assignment or a leisure-time activity. We may "keep after him" or turn him loose.

Diagnosis must lead to action. As mere intellectual exercise it is useless. Consequently, based on our best judgment, we will do *something*. The results determine the validity of our diagnosis and prescription. If all goes well we will proceed to the next learning task. If not, we will reassess our answers to each of the questions, revise our diagnosis and prescription, and try again.

Many people are seeking an instrument that will diagnose, then will "tell us what to do." It is important that we remember this has not been accomplished in any profession that deals with the intricacies of a human being. The thermometer registers with considerable accuracy the temperature of the patient but a doctor must decide which medication to use. In spite of his best and learned judgment, some patients are allergic to the dose and some are beyond his ability to help. Still we have seen tremendous advances in the skill and precision of the medical diagnostician.

As educators, we too are increasing the skill and precision of our assessment of the learner, so we no longer need to keep interminable records and stockpile useless data to stuff cumulative folders. By identification of the critical elements of an assessment we may be sure that instruments will be devised so their objectivity and precision will augment but never replace the highly trained observation that guides educational decisions.

THE EDUCATION
OF INDIVIDUALS

Robert Glaser

Our society is committed to the significance of individual performance, and if we are people of principle, we must act accordingly. To act accordingly requires us to permit the exercise of individual talents and to offer the opportunity to develop and excel in these respects. The problem, so well stated by John W. Gardner,[1] is to provide opportunities and rewards for individuals at every level of ability to realize their potentials and to perform at their best, while at the same time adjusting to society's institutional defenses against excessive emphasis on individual performance. If we accept Gardner's statement of the contesting forces of the rewards for individual performance versus the restraints on individual performance as balancing influences in society, then an educational system which does not allow adequate exercise of individual talents sends out individuals more susceptible to the forces of restraint on their performance than is required for a viable, progressing civilization. It is necessary for an educational system to arrange for the individualized treatment of students; at the same time, invidious distinctions, between students, based upon irrelevant stratification, must be minimized.

Educators are aware of this necessity. Their concern with adapting to the needs of the student is a familiar theme which

Reprinted from Working Paper 12, Learning Research and Development Center, University of Pittsburgh, September, 1964, by permission of Robert Glaser.

[1] John W. Gardner, *Excellence: Can We Be Equal and Excellent Too?* New York: Harper & Brothers, 1961.

has been repeated over and over again and which provides the justification and basic premise for many current educational innovations and experiments. Advances have been instituted for accomplishing this fundamental goal—"track" plans, "continuous progress" plans, team teaching, etc. For the most part, these systems seem never to gather the force to cast off the effects of past practice and organizational inertia. At their best, they remain unique and lauded examples which resist proper dissemination and die, or they become diluted when mixed in the overpowering solution of day-to-day exigencies of school system operation and of pressures on colleges of education to turn out teachers who meet present needs and not new or tomorrow's requirements.

The need is documented and the ideal has been expressed. What do we need to understand about the background, history, pedagogical requirements, psychological facts, technical instructional requirements, and organizational and administrative structures in order to build successful systems for the education of individuals? What underlies our failures in the past and what presently available facts and thinking make our success highly probable at the present time?

GOALS OF INDIVIDUALIZATION

It is useful to examine why individualized forms of instruction appear to be goals worth developing. Other than the platitude of "catering to the needs of the student," what explicity can we look to as educational outcomes worth attaining? First, a system of individualized instruction nurtures independent learning and, as a result, has the potential for producing individuals who are self-resourceful and self-appraising learners. Resourceful individuals of this kind cannot be produced in any significant numbers by our traditional educational environment in which the primary burden of initiating and maintaining learning is the job of the teacher rather than the job of the learner. At the very least, this should be a shared endeavor.

Second, instruction which adapts to individual requirements seems impossible to envision without inclusion of the notions of competence, mastery, and the attainment of standards. Unfettered by the practical necessity for group pacing and for adjustments to a teaching strategy adapted to the group average, it appears necessary for each individual to work to attain a standard of performance which permits him to move on in competence and knowledge. The possibilities of any one individual attaining competence is enhanced since the environment in which he can progress is adapted to his requirements and purposes, undiluted by the frustration of moving ahead with the bright students or the discouragement of just keeping up with the less bright students. In this way, a realistic sense of achievement is developed which encourages the use of one's abilities. The admission to be made is that more than lip service must be paid to the undeniable fact that individuals do differ extensively in their abilities, and our educational system is under obligation to develop an operational capability in line with the facts of human behavior.

OBSTACLES TO INDIVIDUALIZATION

In the development of educational structures that adapt to the individual learner, there have been two primary obstacles: (1) school management structures and their associated teaching practices have been difficult to change under the pressure of practical necessities; and (2) the learning theories upon which educational practices need to be based have been very much devoted to their own growing pains. This growing period has been concerned with carefully controlled experimental studies which lead to the discovery of general and simple laws of behavior—general and simple because, for the most part, the nuances of individual differences in studies of learning have been held constant in order to understand the fundamental processes involved. However, at the present time, the science of psychology is devoting increasing attention to the interaction between individual differences and complex learning phenomena.

PATTERNS OF ADAPTATION TO INDIVIDUAL DIFFERENCES

In education, several major patterns of adapting to individual differences can be identified if one examines past and present educational practices and examines future possibilities.[2] These patterns can be described in terms of the extent to which educational goals and instructional methods have been varied for the handling of individual differences as they appear in the school. One pattern occurs where both educational goals and instructional methods are relatively fixed and inflexible. Individual differences are taken into account chiefly by dropping students along the way. The underlying rationale involved is that every child should "go as far as his abilities warrant." However, a weeding-out process is assumed which is reached earlier or later by different individuals. With this pattern, it is also possible to vary "time to learn" as required for different students. When this is carried out, an individual is permitted to stay in school until he learns certain essential educational outcomes to a specified criterion of achievement. To some extent, this latter practice is carried out in the old policy of keeping a child in the first grade until he can read his primer and in the more recent nongraded primary unit which some children complete in three years, and some in four.

A second pattern of adaptation to individual differences is

[2] See Lee J. Cronbach, "How Can Instruction Be Adapted to Individual Differences?" in Robert Gagné (Ed.), *Learning and Individual Differences*, Merrill Books, 1966.

one in which the prospective future role of a student is determined, and depending upon this role, he is provided with an appropriate curriculum. When this system is in operation, students are channeled into different courses such as academic courses, vocational courses, or business courses; vocationally oriented students get one kind of mathematics and academically oriented students get a different kind of mathematics. Adapting to individual differences by this pattern assumes that an educational system has provision for optional education objectives, but within each option the instructional program is relatively fixed.

A third pattern of adaptation to individual differences varies instructional treatments; different students are taught by different instructional procedures, and the sequence of educational goals is not necessarily common to all students. This pattern can be implemented in different ways. At one extreme, a school can provide a main fixed instructional sequence, and students are branched off from this track for remedial work; when the remedial work is successfully completed, the student is put back into the general track. At the other extreme, there is seemingly the more ideal situation. A school carries out an instructional program which begins by providing detailed diagnosis of the student's learning habits and attitudes, achievements, skills, cognitive style, etc. On the basis of this analysis of the student's characteristics, a prescription is made for a course of instruction specifically tailored to him. Conceivably, in this procedure, students learn in different ways—some by their own discovery, some by more structured methods, some by reading, and some by listening to lectures.

In light of the current experimentation in schools on procedures for adapting to individual differences, it seems likely that in the near future, patterns falling between these two latter extremes will be developed and adopted by many schools. The quality of the various systems developed will depend upon the answers to many questions of research and practical implementation. The entire difficult question of the interaction between the characteristics of a student at a particular point in his learning and appropriate methods of instruction is raised for intensive study. Proof will have to be forthcoming that the instructional methods devised for adapting to individual student differences result in significantly greater attainment of educational goals than less intricate classroom practices or classroom practices where the average best method is employed. Such proof will be accumulated (rather than proved by one crucial experiment) from careful and controlled evaluation of imaginative attacks on the problem.

REQUIREMENTS FOR INDIVIDUALIZATION

It is evident that much of the motion in current educational reform is oriented toward advances in individualizing education. The important question of the moment is whether this activity and the new developments involved will accomplish this objective or whether they will be caught in the inertia of practicality and diffuseness which has stifled similar attempts in the past. Both operating and research experience indicate that certain fundamental requirements for individualization will have to be met if progress along these lines is to be realized. These requirements seem to be the following: [3]

1. The conventional boundaries of grade levels and arbitrary time units for subject matter coverage need to be redesigned to permit each student to work at his actual level of accomplishment in each subject matter area and to permit him to move ahead in each subject as soon as he masters the prerequisites for the next level of advancement.

2. Well-defined sequences of progressive, behaviorally defined objectives in various subject areas need to be established as

[3] Discussions with Professor Glen Heathers of New York University have been quite helpful here.

guidelines for setting up a student's program of study. The student's achievement is defined by his position along this progression of advancement.

3. A student's progress through a curriculum sequence must be monitored by adequate methods and instruments for evaluating his abilities and accomplishments so that a teaching program can be adapted to his requirements and readinesses.

4. Students must be taught and must be provided with appropriate instructional materials so that they acquire increasing competence in self-directed, self-paced learning. In order to accomplish this, the teacher must provide the student with standards of performance so that he can evaluate his own attainment. Primarily, teacher-directed learning must be replaced by teacher-guided, learner-directed accomplishment in order for the goals of individualized education to be achieved.

5. Special professional training must be provided to school personnel so that they can accomplish the evaluation and diagnosis of student performance that is required in order to organize instruction for individualized programs. Teachers must become increasingly competent in the theory and practices of educational diagnosis, evaluation, and guidance. Currently, the teacher is trained in the total class management of learning. In contrast, teachers must now learn how to adapt instruction to subgroups of students and to the individual student.

6. The individualization of instruction requires that the teacher attend to and utilize detailed information about each student in order to design appropriate instructional programs. To assist the teacher in processing this information, it seems likely that schools will take advantage of the unique benefits of automation, and automated data-processing. These systems need to be devised in such a way that

school system personnel can use them comfortably and wisely.

At the present time, it seems possible to develop educational methods that are more sensitive to individual differences than our procedures have been in the past. Educational systems for accomplishing this will no doubt take many forms and have many nuances as they are developed by our educational leaders. In the main, however, it is well to remember that individualization requires the fine honing of instructional procedures so that a student seeks and achieves mastery proceeding along a path, to a large extent, dictated by his own requirements. As a result of a balance between teacher guidance and the student's own self-appraisal, he can follow the path, or blaze the trail, which is neither too difficult nor too easy for him. The teacher in this process will play the significant role of helping the student discover how he learns best; the teacher will need to learn from the learner how to teach, and teach the learner how to learn.

OPEN-STRUCTURE: TOWARD A DESCRIPTION

Helen F. Darrow

Accepting the basic end of education to be the development of self-actualizing, autonomous individuals through means of open-structure learning environments results in a particular kind of individualization—*stress upon independence*. Every school with every teacher participating sees to it, by design, that children learn to experience freedom; and because freedom cannot exist without responsibility, they also see to it that children learn to handle their independence responsibly. "I can choose not to work but I have no right to keep others from working." "If I spend all the time reading, I won't have time to join the playacting group" are the kinds of expressions one might hear as children explore the concept of freedom-responsibility through practice.

As the concept develops, it seems reasonable to expect children more and more to perceive schools as a legitimate place to make learning decisions (choices). This involves learning to use time, space, and resources effectively for individual purposes. Choosing what to do, when to do it, where and why become legitimate problems to solve in the school setting. Children demonstrate awareness of some choice-making dimensions when they say, "Frank and Walter and I want to make up a questionnaire to check out people's prejudices

Adapted and reprinted from *Individualization of Instruction: Exploring Open-Structure*, Los Angeles: California [ASUCLA Students' Store, 308 Westwood Plaza], 1968, pp. 7–24, with the permission of Helen Fisher Darrow.

about skin color. We're reading an opinion poll report in the newspaper and we think we ought to see how our kids feel." Or "I'm going to the Writing Center to write a story. I might call it 'The Talking Chair' but it will take just a short time to do because it's already in my head." In such a school environment children's perceptions should easily extend to awareness of themselves as able competent learners who feel good about themselves and their accomplishments. "I can sing real good and read OK but I can't cross the horizontal bars very well" reveals self-felt limitations along with recognized strengths and talents. If the child adds: "I'm going to have to get more used to swinging from the bars," he is also indicating interest in improvement.

Learning to meet inner psychological needs through contacts with outer social realities should indeed enable children to experience what Krishnamurti describes as true education. "To understand life is to understand ourselves and that is both the beginning and end of education." [1] In this respect school becomes both a place of security and a place for risk-taking. Children learn to face the unknown willingly as they become free to explore the learning environment in direct experiences with "raw" materials for learning. As they do, one might well hear such expressions as: "I think I'll take my shoes off and stomp on this clay to see if I can mold it better"; and "I wonder what will happen when I disconnect this wire"; and "Yes, I'll do the part of the witch and make up my own dance for it, but I've never done it before."

Self-actualization and autonomy, however, cannot be achieved in isolation from others. In an open-structure learning environment children can be expected to operate within a democratic framework of personal-social values. Philip Phenix has elaborated upon four enduring values for all Americans: intelligence, creativity, conscience, and reverence. *Intelligence* he explains as the experience of thinking

[1] J. Krishnamurti, *Education and the Significance of Life*, Harper, 1953, p. 14.

clearly, making decisions, using critical judgment. *Creativity* he describes as the functioning of man as maker, productive worker, zestful player who experiments and constructs and enjoys labor. *Conscience* becomes the respect of man for man, the building of self-giving devotion to causes for the improvement of mankind. Social-economic class lines, grouping procedures, and other means of separating man from man, child from child are avoided. And *reverence* moves individuals beyond their own small lives and frail institutions to a sense of the grandeur and awe beyond grasp.[2]

Children living within such a framework should not only deepen their understanding of democratic values but, having experienced them in practice, should apply them in daily life. As children interact and confront one another, and are encouraged to do so, they can also engage in a meeting of the minds—toward solution of problems and attainment of goals, both individual and group. Here are some ways children have described individual-group help:

Once a little girl had trouble getting a paper up on the board. A boy came along and said: "May I help you?" "Of course," answered the girl.

The children wanted to fix up their classroom because it didn't look very nice. They painted pictures, made posters, put things away. The teacher was surprised and said: "Thank you."

The committees made different things for one project. Those that didn't read so well drew or built something or learned by working with the others. The mural will help them all remember better. They tried to make a good committee so they could have friends. It's no fun when you don't have friends to help you.

With personal-social values like these dominating the school culture, school life can be expected to take on a high positive value for children. As they experience in school an "open society" where pluralism and diversity flourish, children should be able to find school a place which supports their

[2] Philip Phenix, "Values in the Emerging American Civilization," *Teachers College Record*, Vol. 16, No. 7, April 1960, pp. 355–366.

being individual personalities and *becoming* self-actualizing autonomous persons. None of these outcomes, or others, emerges by haphazard encounters. Those who seek the outcomes must develop them, planning and executing their design carefully, conscientiously, and competently.

LEARNING OPPORTUNITIES

In open-structure learning situations there are few if any prescribed materials and resources for individuals and groups. Materials and resources are not reserved for certain grades, certain children, certain teachers. (Choices for learning experiences are always limited, of course, by what teachers and children can envision and carry out.) Field trips, for example, are encouraged whenever and wherever they can be used as an educational activity. They may occur weekly, monthly, occasionally, intermittently. They may occur daily for a while across the school yard to observe changes in the magnolia trees and to record observations. Inner City may be bus-toured by Suburbanites to become a data-source for speculating upon contrasting living conditions. Whatever the trip, individuals have the right to join the group or not, as they wish.

Materials are used similarly. An art-center studio may contain a variety of art media to be used whenever individuals or groups elect to work there. Tempera paints, watercolors, yarns, clay, textiles, paper assortments—particular materials available may vary at any one time according to individual and group purposes. Other center studios provide other kinds of choices from writing areas to science and music areas or mathematics centers. When the environment also includes a range of machines—slide, filmstrip and film projectors, tape recorders, typewriters, record players—and supplies to accompany their use, as well as quantities of printed materials— library books, textbooks, magazines, charts, original storybooks—the possibilities for individual preferences in learning styles obviously increase. Children studying phonetic skills then can choose to do so through tape recordings, records, filmstrips, workbook pages, games, or with a peer group and teacher at the blackboard—or any combination of these.

Choices of learning opportunities involve not only differences in learning styles but dimensions of what, when, where, and why. Choosing questions to study, topics to pursue, skills to practice become matters of individual-teacher-group planning, rather than authoritarian decree or arbitrary assignment. Choosing when to read, when to study, when to work at the music center or math center, or deciding how long to spend on a topic and where best to work emerge as problems for individuals to recognize and resolve, with or without teacher help.

Discussions take on special importance as learning opportunities in open-structure learning situations. Not only do they serve the purpose of exploring choices but also of settling management problems, launching planning-evaluation sessions, and encouraging the inquiry process.

PROCESS OF INQUIRY

As children freely discuss their thoughts and feelings, they can build a personalized basis for inquiry. In so doing each child inquires into his own questions or questions from others which stimulate him to inquiry; he interacts directly with primary sources of information to gather and examine data for reflective thinking and comes to his own conclusions—if conclusions are warranted—or to his own level of understanding and insight. A small group of young boys, for example, began to inquire in this fashion:

We ought to make a map of Traveltown so we can explain to people where we were last week. Let's see—How do you make a map? What kind of map are you going to make? Let's look at different kinds of maps to see what kind we want. What do these different maps show? How do you read them? We can ask our fathers to help us read this road map. How do we know which direction we went, and how do we show directions on a map? Why do we need to show directions? How will people know we went by bus? How will they know what we saw? How do maps show that? The trains and other things didn't move the way the bus and we and the teacher did. Maybe we should paint them on and make the movable things separately. How can we show how far we've really been? That trip took more than half an hour, but the freeway made a real difference in the time it took. How long would it take using the city streets instead of the freeway? How are different kinds of roads shown so people will know which ones are faster?

And so children's inquiry into map-making with its space-time relationships grew and consolidated as they attempted to reach their goal—a usable map of the trip.

The inquiry approach used as the major method in open-structure reverses the sequence of "teaching steps" traditionally used—an assignment to read, closed-structured questions formed by the teacher and recited by pupils, followed by perhaps a quiz and then an "enrichment" activity or craft production. Instead, it relies upon feelings of curiosity and urges to explore; it feeds upon unorganized data collected by the learner himself, to be organized by the learner and used for further questions or inferences and perhaps generalizations. The cycle is endless. There is always more to learn, more to explore so long as the learner himself responds to the urge. Throughout the experience the child maintains control over his inquiry. He himself functions as investigator, experimenter, questioner, examiner, explorer—and discoverer. In the process he should gain useful knowledge.

KNOWLEDGE

Knowledge in open-structure learning environments is closely identified with processes of study and with unifying ideas related to discipline structures and interrelationships among disciplines. Conclusions are seen as outcomes of inquiry. The stress then is twofold: upon *how* knowledge is accumulated and upon *what* big ideas can be uncovered to bring a sense of order to understanding the world. Inquiry is not merely to discover what the investigator did and thought, but to understand what the thoughts and actions contributed to the inquiry.

To achieve this kind of knowledge, children need to experience for themselves the "tools" used by various kinds of scholars. Developing questionnaires, conducting surveys, compiling results into organized retrieval charts move children into the work of social scientists. Analyzing variations in city growth charts, hypothesizing conditions affecting population settlements and applying knowledge claims to explanations of city growths enable children to function as "geographers." [3] And so with the work of other investigators—scientists, artists, musicians, mathematicians. When these various discipline structures are interrelated by dealing with modern social problems—poverty, prejudice, friendship, and a host of others—children have the opportunity to look at the "wholeness" of things not otherwise possible.[4]

Experiencing the methodologies of discipline-building however is not enough. Children also need opportunities to develop key concepts and values growing out of their explorations. Some of these include appreciating human differences, understanding justice as a force in human life, being aware of the interdependence of mankind, and comprehending the balances in nature. The kinds of understandings gained become personalized as children pursue individual interests

[3] Charlotte Crabtree, "Stimulating Reflective Thinking in the Classroom," *Effective Thinking in the Social Studies*, 37th Yearbook, National Council for the Social Studies, 1967, pp. 77–122.

[4] See suggestions for study in *Toward Social Studies Understandings* by Helen Darrow, Teachers College Press, 1964.

and concerns. Even when groups share similar concerns individuals are free to seek their own levels of understanding. Each child adds to his knowledge system only those strands which have meaning for him and those ideas which have relevance for his own personal-social life. Neither covering particular topics or subject areas nor expecting children to arrive at identical meanings and understandings has a place in the open-structure learning environment.

As with the inquiry process there is no end to what children might gain in knowledge as they go deeper and deeper to explore their questions and curiosities. Here the teacher has a vital role to play.

TEACHER PARTICIPATION

It seems reasonable to expect the quality of both inquiry and knowledge-experiencing by learners to be improved with the participation of the teacher. Insights should become clarified, alternatives examined, hypotheses raised, and further plans for investigation made through teacher-led discussions and conferences.

Thelen suggests a three-pronged responsibility for the teacher in encouraging inquiry: first, *stimulating* inquiry and investigation; second, *arranging* for individuals and small groups to interact at thinking-feeling levels; and third, *guiding* reflective thinking to build deeper meanings and clearer values.[5] In the open-structure learning environments, open-ended questions function as a major key to inquiry: Why do you think that? What would happen if you changed? How can you explain that? How do you intend to prove your point? What do you plan to do next? What materials do you need? Questions like these help children to explore divergent

[5] Herbert Thelen, "Some Classroom Quiddities for People-Oriented Teachers," *Journal of Behavioral Science*, Vol. 1, No. 3, 1965.

thinking where many kinds of answers are possible. In this sense the teacher's role becomes crucial to the direction of individual inquiry and understanding.

The teacher who brings materials into the environment with the hope of stimulating inquiry—say about properties of H_2O —rightfully raises such comments and questions as "Some of you might be interested in what I have here for some experimentation with water. What might you do with these materials (or others you can find yourself) to make some discoveries about water? How will you record your work? your observations? How can you help others to replicate your experiments?"

During discussions of discoveries made over a period of time, the teacher continues to be responsible for raising questions: "How did you get that conclusion? Will such an object always float? What made the difference? Suppose you changed the container?" and on and on, helping children to explore more deeply than they might without teacher guidance.

Discussions and seminars enable both teacher and children to interact, sharing ways of working as well as findings—clarifying ideas, developing ideas, recognizing new problems, and planning next steps. At times discussions may lead to making judgments and inferences, generalizations, or further knowledge claims to be tested out.

Even though individuals study varied topics or work at varied tasks, they can explore common concepts and skills in group settings. Individuals, for example, selecting to study the habits of ants might discuss insect social life under teacher direction with those examining the world of cockroaches or bees; children studying particular insects might join with those studying other animals—including man—in a discussion of "community life." Not only does the teacher accept responsibility for increasing the quality of experiences for children, but she takes the lead in arranging the environment for productive interactions.

GROUPING

Any hour of the school day might reveal fluid groupings like five or six individuals conferring about plans to develop an aerial map of the valley, partners developing original ABC books, three or four children seated together listening to a story read by another child or to a record, seven or eight children seated at a table developing equations in mathematics using Cuisenaire rods under teacher direction, three or four children helping each other practice spelling and handwriting at the blackboard, four or five children painting a mural of "Saturday on Our Block" to use as a prop for an original play, two partners sculpturing a clay circus representing Seuss characters, and other children working alone on independent tasks.

Groupings are usually formed not by general ability or age levels but by specific skill need, by common interests, or by tasks requiring diversity of talents. At times individuals choose to work alone; at other times they may choose to work with a few others; at still other times they prefer to join a larger group discussion or listening session. While the choice is frequently the child's, there are times of course when the teacher deliberately arranges groups to work under his supervision. Teachers may request four or five children having common difficulties to come together for specific practice and help. Particular children may be called together for the purpose of taking a test, practicing the use of homonyms, developing the concept of regrouping in subtraction. Small groups are formed to discuss skills used in selecting a book to read, or common problems like interference with the rights of others or inability to handle materials with care.

Thus, in the open-structure learning environment, groups are temporary and constantly changing. Group work begins with a clear goal (or with the clear purpose of establishing one), and ends with completion of the goal. When there is reason to get together, either because some children intend to work together or because the teacher hopes to pursue a common problem, arrangements can be made with both the teacher and children developing the plans. Predetermined, rigidly scheduled grouping plans are avoided, especially homogeneous class groupings and rigid ability level groupings. Because pluralism and diversity are basic aspects of an open-structure learning environment, children of various ages and abilities are deliberately brought together into "class groups."

In such cross-age groupings, two or more teachers may decide to plan and work together to provide even a greater range of choice-making and inquiry opportunities than might be otherwise available. Team teaching makes this possible. But the emphasis is upon cooperative effort to sustain individual growth. In groupings which capitalize upon individuality, there can be no such organization as "first grade group work" or "below grade level" reading groups. Nor can there be such occurrences as displacement of a child who reads "too well" to remain in his class; or "extra" activities like typing for "advanced" groups who early met prescribed grade requirements. In short, because the emphasis is upon individual growth, class groupings based upon age or grade level expectations become meaningless. Concepts like "remediation for slow learners" and "enrichment for gifted children" have little meaning in the open-structure learning environment, where continuous progress becomes the focus of both planning and evaluation.

PLANNING AND EVALUATION

Teachers and children and others involved constantly note changes in behavior, thinking, attitudes, values, performance, whatever, in terms of the basic goal—development of self-actualizing, autonomous persons. To note some of these changes, teachers and children can together examine samples of work and records of performance scores over a period of time. When children maintain their own records insomuch as possible, when they retain files and charts of successfully completed work, performance scores, and project reports, they have evidence for determining their own growth. In this way self-evaluation is stressed.

Teachers, of course, have responsibility also to assess growth and to discuss their findings with children. Not only can they share testing results, but they can share observations and interpretations of introspective evidence. This means that teachers will have taken the time to observe children during informal interactions with other children as well as during more formal occasions. It means too that the teacher will use some projective techniques like picture discussions and incompleted sentences and stories to uncover some underlying attitudes and values of children, and thus broaden the scope of assessment.

Regardless of evaluation instruments used, evaluation in the open-structure learning environment remains highly individualized. Because of this the teacher's primary responsibility in evaluation is to find ways to help the child focus upon his own personal growth toward self-direction. Questions raised during individual and group evaluation conferences often help: What did you accomplish this week? What kind of progress have you made? How satisfied are you with what you did? Why? What can you do to improve? What do you need to work on next?

Children who are achieving growth toward autonomy might respond in ways like these:

I outlined the ideas for my book and will be ready to talk with you about getting started on the first chapter. I think I've got a very interesting plot going.

I still don't understand equations starting with an empty set. Could I join the group you're working with on that?

I can write stories on my own now and I don't get nervous just because I don't know exactly how to spell a word I need. I just spell it best I can. But I do want you after I'm done to help me make a spelling list so I can study the words I don't know.

Evaluation, of course, carries little meaning without attention to goal-setting. In the open-structure learning environment, the learner has much to say about the goals to be achieved.

Only when the learner actively participates in setting his goals and planning ways to achieve his goals can he carry the major responsibility for assessing his learning. Then he is in the position to "see for himself" where is he going and how he will get there.

I want to work on my d's and t's today to see if I can make them more legible.

If I practice the story of three bears I can read it to the kindergartners.

We're going to try to build a weather station to see if we really can predict weather accurately—or at least to see how accurately we can predict the weather.

I'm looking for a book that will make a good puppet play.

Some of these goals are completely self-determined; others are generated through individual and group interests. Some are generated through interactions with peers or by conferences with teachers. Since the teacher is seeking self-direction for the child, directions for goals in the latter case should emerge as specific work is discussed or checked; and whenever possible the child himself is encouraged to suggest next steps to take for his improvement.

New goals emerge as older goals are evaluated; thus planning, like evaluation, becomes a continuous process with both teacher and learner participating in decisions to be made. Learning to record plans and use them for evaluation purposes becomes an important way to relate planning and evaluating to goal attainment.

In the open-structure learning environment, the process of

goal-setting-planning-executing-evaluating is an endless process with one goal leading to another as the learner takes his own individual strides toward becoming a self-actualizing, autonomous person. Individualization in this framework functions indeed as an open-ended conception. The learner's possibilities for growth are endless.

FREEDOM
AND LEARNING:
THE NEED FOR CHOICE

Paul Goodman

The belief that a highly industrialized society requires twelve to twenty years of prior processing of the young is an illusion or a hoax. The evidence is strong that there is no correlation between school performance and life achievement in any of the professions, whether medicine, law, engineering, journalism, or business. Moreover, recent research shows that for more modest clerical, technological, or semiskilled factory jobs there is no advantage in years of schooling or the possession of diplomas. We were not exactly savages in 1900 when only 6 per cent of adolescents graduated from high school.

Whatever the deliberate intention, schooling today serves mainly for policing and for taking up the slack in youth unemployment. It is not surprising that the young are finally rebelling against it, especially since they cannot identify with the goals of so much social engineering—for instance, that 86 per cent of the federal budget for research and development is for military purposes.

We can, I believe, educate the young entirely in terms of their free choice, with no processing whatever. Nothing can be efficiently learned, or, indeed, learned at all—other than through parroting or brute training, when acquired knowledge is promptly forgotten after the examination—unless it

Reprinted from *Saturday Review*, Vol. 51, May 18, 1968, pp. 73–75, with the permission of the author and the publisher. Copyright 1968 Saturday Review, Inc.

meets need, desire, curiosity, or fantasy. Unless there is a reaching from within, the learning cannot become "second nature," as Aristotle called true learning. It seems stupid to decide a priori what the young ought to know and then to try to motivate them, instead of letting the initiative come from them and putting information and relevant equipment at their service. It is false to assert that this kind of freedom will not serve society's needs—at least those needs that should humanly be served; freedom is the only way toward authentic citizenship and real, rather than verbal, philosophy. Free choice is not random but responsive to real situations; both youth and adults live in a nature of things, a polity, an ongoing society, and it is these, in fact, that attract interest and channel need. If the young, as they mature, can follow their bent and choose their topics, times, and teachers, and if teachers teach what they themselves consider important—which is all they can skillfully teach anyway—the needs of society will be adequately met; there will be more lively, independent, and inventive people; and in the fairly short run there will be a more sensible and efficient society.

It is not necessary to argue for free choice as a metaphysical proposition; it is what is indicated by present conditions. Increasingly, the best young people resolutely resist authority, and we will let them have a say or lose them. And more important, since the conditions of modern social and technological organization are so pervasively and rigidly conforming, it is necessary, in order to maintain human initiative, to put our emphasis on protecting the young from top-down direction. The monkish and academic methods which were civilizing for wild shepherds create robots in a period of high technology. The public schools which did a good job of socializing immigrants in an open society now regiment individuals and rigidify class stratification.

Up to age twelve, there is no point to formal subjects or a prearranged curriculum. With guidance, whatever a child experiences is educational. Dewey's idea is a good one: It makes no difference *what* is learned at this age, so long as the child goes on wanting to learn something further. Teachers for this age are those who like children, pay attention to them, answer their questions, enjoy taking them around the city and helping them explore, imitate, try out, and who sing songs with them and teach them games. Any benevolent grownup—literate or illiterate—has plenty to teach an eight-year-old; the only profitable training for teachers is a group therapy and, perhaps, a course in child development.

We see that infants learn to speak in their own way in an environment where there is speaking and where they are addressed and take part. If we tried to teach children to speak according to our own theories and methods and schedules, as we try to teach reading, there would be as many stammerers as there are bad readers. Besides, it has been shown that whatever is useful in the present eight-year elementary curriculum can be learned in four months by a normal child of twelve. If let alone, in fact, he will have learned most of it by himself.

Since we have communities where people do not attend to the children as a matter of course, and since children must be rescued from their homes, for most of these children there should be some kind of school. In a proposal for mini-schools in New York City, I suggested an elementary group of twenty-eight children with four grownups: a licensed teacher, a housewife who can cook, a college senior, and a teen-age school dropout. Such a group can meet in any store front, church basement, settlement house, or housing project; more important, it can often go about the city, as is possible when the student-teacher ratio is 7 to 1. Experience at the First Street School in New York has shown that the cost for such a little school is less than for the public school with a student-teacher ratio of 30 to 1. (In the public system, most of the money goes for administration and for specialists to remedy the lack of contact in the classroom.) As A. S. Neill has shown, attendance need not be compulsory. The school should be located near home so the children can escape from it to home, and from home to it. The school should be supported by public money but administered entirely by its own children, teachers, and parents.

In the adolescent and college years, the present mania is to keep students at their lessons for another four to ten years as the only way of their growing up in the world. The correct policy would be to open as many diverse paths as possible, with plenty of opportunity to backtrack and change. It is said by James Conant that about 15 per cent learn well by books and study in an academic setting, and these can opt for high school. Most, including most of the bright students, do better either on their own or as apprentices in activities that are for keeps, rather than through lessons. If their previous eight years had been spent in exploring their own bents and interests, rather than being continually interrupted to do others' assignments on others' schedules, most adolescents would have a clearer notion of what they are after, and many would have found their vocations.

For the 15 per cent of adolescents who learn well in schools and are interested in subjects that are essentially academic, the present catch-all high schools are wasteful. We would do better to return to the small preparatory academy, with perhaps sixty students and three teachers—one in physical sciences, one in social sciences, one in humanities—to prepare for college board examinations. An academy could be located in, and administered by, a university and staffed by graduate students who like to teach and in this way might earn stipends while they write their theses. In such a setting, without dilution by nonacademic subjects and a mass of uninterested fellow students, an academic adolescent can, by spending three hours a day in the classroom, easily be prepared in three or four years for college.

Forcing the nonacademic to attend school breaks the spirit of most and foments alienation in the best. Kept in tutelage, young people, who are necessarily economically dependent, cannot pursue the sexual, adventurous, and political activities congenial to them. Since lively youngsters insist on these anyway, the effect of what we do is to create a gap between them and the oppressive adult world, with a youth subculture and an arrested development.

School methods are simply not competent to teach all the arts, sciences, professions, and skills the school establishment pretends to teach. For some professions—e.g., social work, architecture, pedagogy—trying to earn academic credits is probably harmful because it is an irrelevant and discouraging obstacle course. Most technological know-how has to be learned in actual practice in offices and factories, and this often involves unlearning what has been laboriously crammed for exams. The technical competence required by skilled and semiskilled workmen and average technicians can be acquired in three weeks to a year on the job, with no previous schooling. The importance of even "functional literacy" is much exaggerated; it is the attitude, and not the reading ability, that counts. Those who are creative in the arts and sciences almost invariably go their own course and are usually hampered by schools. Modern languages are best learned by travel. It is pointless to teach social sciences, literary criticism, and philosophy to youngsters who have had no responsible experience in life and society.

Most of the money now spent for high schools and colleges should be devoted to the support of apprenticeships; travel; subsidized browsing in libraries and self-directed study and research; programs such as VISTA, the Peace Corps, Students for a Democratic Society, or the Student Nonviolent Coordinating Committee; rural reconstruction; and work camps for projects in conservation and urban renewal. It is a vast sum of money—but it costs almost $1,500 a year to keep a youth in a blackboard jungle in New York; the schools have become one of our major industries. Consider one kind of opportunity. Since it is important for the very existence of the republic to countervail the now overwhelming national corporate style of information, entertainment, and research, we need scores of thousands of small independent television stations, community radio stations, local newspapers that are more than gossip notes and ads, community theaters, high-brow or dissenting magazines, small design offices for neighborhood renewal that is not bureaucratized, small laboratories for science and invention that are not centrally directed. Such enterprises could present admirable opportunities for bright but unacademic young people to serve as apprentices.

Ideally, the polis itself is the educational environment; a good community consists of worthwhile, attractive, and fulfilling callings and things to do, to grow up into. The policy I am proposing tends in this direction rather than away from it. By multiplying options, it should be possible to find an interesting course for each individual youth, as we now do for only some of the emotionally disturbed and the troublemakers. Voluntary adolescent choices are often random and foolish and usually transitory; but they are the likeliest ways of growing up reasonably. What is most essential is for the youth to see that he is taken seriously as a person, rather than fitted into an institutional system. I don't know if this tailor-made approach would be harder or easier to administer than standardization that in fact fits nobody and results in an increasing number of recalcitrants. On the other hand, as the Civilian Conservation Corps showed in the Thirties, the products of willing youth labor can be valuable even economically, whereas accumulating Regents blue-books is worth nothing except to the school itself.

(By and large, it is not in the adolescent years but in later years that, in all walks of life, there is need for academic withdrawal, periods of study and reflection, synoptic review of the texts. The Greeks understood this and regarded most of our present college curricula as appropriate for only those over the age of thirty or thirty-five. To some extent, the churches used to provide a studious environment. We do these things miserably in hurried conferences.)

We have similar problems in the universities. We cram the young with what they do not want at the time and what most of them will never use; but by requiring graded diplomas we make it hard for older people to get what they want and can use. Now, paradoxically, when so many are going to school, the training of authentic learned professionals is proving to be a failure, with dire effects on our ecology, urbanism, polity, communications, and even the direction of science. Doing others' lessons under compulsion for twenty years does not tend to produce professionals who are autonomous, principled, and ethically responsible to client and community. Broken by processing, professionals degenerate to mere professional-personnel. Professional peer groups have become economic lobbies. The licensing and maintenance of standards have been increasingly relinquished to the state, which has no competence.

In licensing professionals, we have to look more realistically at functions, drop mandarin requirements of academic diplomas that are irrelevant, and rid ourselves of the ridiculous fad of awarding diplomas for every skill and trade whatever. In most professions and arts there are important abstract parts that can best be learned academically. The natural procedure is for those actually engaged in a professional activity to go to school to learn what they now know they need; re-entry into the academic track, therefore, should be made easy for those with a strong motive.

Universities are primarily schools of learned professions, and the faculty should be composed primarily not of academics but of working professionals who feel duty-bound and attracted to pass on their tradition to apprentices of a new generation. Being combined in a community of scholars, such professionals teach a noble apprenticeship, humane and with vision toward a more ideal future. It is humane because the disciplines communicate with one another; it is ideal because the young are free and questioning. A good professional school can be tiny. In *The Community of Scholars* I suggest that 150 students and ten professionals—the size of the usual medieval university—are enough. At current faculty salaries, the cost per student would be a fourth of that of our huge administrative machines. And, of course, on such a small scale contact between faculty and students is sought for and easy.

Today, because of the proved incompetence of our adult institutions and the hypocrisy of most professionals, university students have a right to a large say in what goes on. (But this, too, is medieval.) Professors will, of course, teach what they please. My advice to students is that given by Prince Kropotkin, in "A Letter to the Young": "Ask what kind of world do you want to live in? What are you good at and want to work at to build that world? What do you need to know? Demand that your teachers teach you that." Serious teachers would be delighted by this approach.

The idea of the liberal arts college is a beautiful one: to teach the common culture and refine character and citizenship. But it does not happen; the evidence is that the college curriculum has little effect on underlying attitudes, and most cultivated folk do not become so by this route. School friendships and the community of youth do have lasting effects, but these do not require ivyed clubhouses. Young men learn more about the theory and practice of government by resisting the draft than they ever learned in Political Science 412.

Much of the present university expansion, needless to say, consists in federal- and corporation-contracted research and other research and has nothing to do with teaching. Surely such expansion can be better carried on in the Government's and corporations' own institutes, which would be unencumbered by the young, except those who are hired or attach themselves as apprentices.

Every part of education can be open to need, desire, choice, and trying out. Nothing needs to be compelled or extrinsically motivated by prizes and threats. I do not know if the procedure here outlined would cost more than our present system—though it is hard to conceive of a need for more money than the school establishment now spends. What would be saved is the pitiful waste of youthful years—caged, daydreaming, sabotaging, and cheating—and the degrading and insulting misuse of teachers.

It has been estimated by James Coleman that the average youth in high school is really "there" about ten minutes a day. Since the growing-up of the young into society to be useful to themselves and others, and to do God's work, is one of the three or four most important functions of any society, no doubt we ought to spend even more on the education of the young than we do; but I would not give a penny to the present administrators, and I would largely dismantle the present school machinery.

PART III
Programs and Practices

As teachers experiment with individualization of instruction there will be problems to solve, ways of working to be modified, techniques and methods to be developed, and extensive planning and evaluation to be carried on. The learning environment will become a responsive one, learner-centered, with characteristics of flexibility, variety, openness, activity, inquiry, and experimentation. Organization and structure will release children to learn; to practice self-direction. Classrooms will be less tidy and less logical from an external viewpoint. A vast array of materials will be found—raw materials brought in by children, materials produced by children, materials which children can handle to observe functions, patterns, and relationships. And management procedures and arrangements will be flexible, changing to meet new demands, new interests, new needs. The classroom program will continually evolve and develop as the teacher and children are caught up in the joy and excitement of learning. It is, then, within this framework that illustrative examples of programs and practices can have meaning and be of value to the teacher.

INDIVIDUALIZED INSTRUCTION: A CLASSROOM SCENE

Virgil M. Howes

The classroom was like a beehive. Workers were busily engaged in all kinds of activity. There was noise. There were children moving about. The teacher and one child sat alone talking. Ten names remained on the blackboard behind them. A small group seemed to be playing games on the floor. Two readers sat at a table facing each other. A future artist came in from her easel just outside the door. Tim, or so said the name on the paper, was doing math—something to do with sets, I believe. Three children with head phones were listening to a tape. A filmslide projector's image held the interest of a small blond operator and her friend. And no one paid any attention to me!

I was seeing individualization of instruction in action—the kind of individualization that creates an open-structure for learning; a teaching strategy which focuses on pupil direction and self-control matched with pupil management and responsibility. Self-selection, self-guidance, and self-discipline—were they mottos over the door through which I'd entered?

The physical space was a series of nooks and crannies, corners, and interest centers created by putting two file drawers here, a portable blackboard there, a bookshelf at right angles to that wall, and some boxes stacked to make a screen. Tables and chairs scattered, grouped in pairs, arranged in

Reprinted from *Individualization of Instruction: Exploring Open-Structure*, Virgil M. Howes, et al., Los Angeles, California [ASUCLA Students' Store, 308 Westwood Plaza], 1968, pp. 1–6.

squares completed the maze. But each area, whether it was for one or six, had a special appeal—the listening post, the art corner (though easels all seemed to be outside), the game room (educational, of course), the reading nook, the filmslide "tunnel," the study-work tables, and on and on. A square classroom of uncluttered space, indeed! An area holding surprises and interests, crammed with goodies, yes!

From the front blackboard, I read

9:00– 9:30	P.E.
9:30–11:30	Conferences
12:30– 1:00	Class
1:00– 2:30	Conferences

Not much of a daily schedule until Susan explained and showed me her plan. All the children had taken P.E. as a group that day. (It was now 10:45.) "Conferences" meant the teacher was available to individuals at the time listed—nearly the entire day. Anyone wanting a conference wrote his name on the board and listed the subject such as math, reading, and social studies.

"Class, 12:30–1:00," meant a time when the teacher gave some directions to the class as a whole. Children raised questions about work in general, clarified committee arrangements, discussed the learning environment, and gained clearer understandings of the day's work. And finally, it was a time when each child completed his schedule for the next day—the time he chose for doing reading, social studies, math, handwriting, spelling.

The blackboard schedule might read differently tomorrow than today. The teacher posts her schedule each day. This schedule tells the class how the teacher plans to use her time and notes total class activities for the day. The schedule has time blocks which vary according to the activity or teacher strategy planned. On some days, the blocks may largely be "conference." On other days, it may include "small groups" for planning, for writing, or for evaluating.

Class P.E. is usually scheduled. Music may be total class as social studies might. The children's progress, the children's needs and interests, the special opportunities of the day are all considered as the teacher makes her schedule and posts it on the blackboard. This becomes the framework for individual pupil schedules. Each child can see at a glance the kind of specific teacher resource available and the "musts" of the day. He selects and adds until his personal schedule is completed.

(Later, in looking at Tim's schedule, I noted he scheduled one period of "do nothing.")

Each child keeps his own schedule for ready reference in a file folder he has made. (Some teachers prefer children to use a notebook.) No bells ring, but children go from one activity to the next by being their own time-keepers. And if interest and concentration are so great that a scheduled activity is missed, there's always tomorrow. Who wants to stop in the middle of an important task?

Daily schedules are filed in a folder for each child under his name. (He does the filing.) These are available to the teacher and to the child as a ready reference to what a week, a month, or yesterday was like. These are data for a child in planning future activities, for pupil-teacher conferences, for parent discussions, for pupil-pupil discussions and comparisons.

When was reading taught? For John, it was from 9:30 to 10:15. He had his name on the board for a conference, I noted. Michele was going to read from 1:30 to 2:00. Rachel chose 10:15 to 11:00. Reading was any time—it was individualized. Yesterday, I learned, the "teacher's" blackboard schedule had included small group sessions. There was a variety of small groups with specific purposes described. Interests, practice, sharing, testing, project development, and enjoyment were beginning points for organizing the groups. Some groups had been focused on reading problems. The teacher had encouraged five children having common difficulties to come together for specific instruction and help. Others had concentrated on math. Still others were working in social studies. Such sessions occurred frequently during the week. Sometimes children organized the group; sometimes the teacher organized it. Children moved in and out as needs and interests dictated. Group size varied with the task and immediate demands.

"Are you having a conference today?" I asked Lyn.

"No."

"Did you yesterday?"

"No," she again replied.

"Will you tomorrow?" I queried.

"Maybe," she said.

"And what if you don't for several days?" I continued.

"Well," Lyn said, "the teacher would eventually write your name on the board. You see, she keeps track, so if you forget, after awhile, she asks you to come!"

At the next table, four children seemed to be having a wonderful time. There was even an occasional giggle. Surely, I thought, the teacher would intervene. If she didn't, I was sure the group of four would soon attract others. But I was wrong. No one seemed to mind. Everyone was busy except them. I eased over to find out more. And then it became clear —the four were working. They were adapting a story they had read about Greece into a play for the class. As Marti explained, class members shared with each other in many ways. Sometimes it was with the whole class. At other times, it might be among special friends or maybe with the teacher at conference time. And sometimes, small groups got together spontaneously (that was the meaning but not the word she used). Learning, discoveries, questions, plans, progress—all were things to share in different ways, at different times, with different groups or individuals.

Why, this wasn't school at all, I thought. School was where children went to learn—at times and in ways decided by adults. Wasn't it too risky to leave such choices to children? How could they know what was good for them? What if they missed some important learning because their choice hadn't included it?

But the children had answers to my questions: What are you doing? Why did you do that? What will you do? What did you do? They seemed to know what they were about.

Maybe this is what school is about. Maybe here children were learning about how to learn.

HOW YOU CAN INDIVIDUALIZE INSTRUCTION – RIGHT NOW

Dwight W. Allen

TIME WAIVERS

These waivers merely permit flexible examination or assignment deadlines. If we're going to individualize instruction, why does everything have to be turned in on Friday at 2? It isn't really a big deal to let some kids turn in their work the following Monday or Tuesday—or a few days early. Isn't it more important to find out what he knows rather than what he knows on Friday?

School administrators are preoccupied with organizational considerations. It's very convenient for the organization to have everything turned in at 2 o'clock on Friday. I was guilty of that as a teacher because I used to hate to have tag ends. It wasn't that I minded so much the student turning in the project late; it was the problem of putting the project with the rest of the stack so I could eventually grade them together. It was just messy. Let's solve the administrative problem as such and not confuse it with teaching and learning. One of many possible solutions is to have nonprofessional personnel available to receive and sort them. To get time waivers going suggest to your faculty members that they systematically explore changing the pattern of due dates to individualize in-

Reprinted from *Nation's Schools*, Vol. 81, April 1968, pp. 43–46ff., by permission of the publisher.

struction or let students select their own due dates within reasonable limits for projects and for examinations. Eliminate "surprise quizzes," which accomplish little more than dramatizing the teacher as a formidable antagonist.

COOPERATIVE STUDENT EFFORTS

This approach divides student labor and leads to a cumulative effort on assignments or tests. Sometimes you can take incorrigible students who really produce virtually nothing on tests and convince them they're getting away with something if you let them work together. You're really not jeopardizing much if you pick five students who are likely to come up with an F on an examination and allow them to put their efforts together.

This won't work with everybody. Some students react well; some don't. But I think schools have to get over the notion that is firmly ingrained in them—that education is a unique and individual competitive effort. It is a little unreal to train students competitively to go out in society and perform cooperatively.

School faculties might want to say, in effect: *O.K., let's each agree that at some time during the year we will try some sort of cooperative student effort, some sort of collaboration. And at the end of the year, we'll get together and share the results and see what worked and what didn't work and how we might want to push the experiment out a little further another time around.* This is a simple way of injecting some substance into faculty meetings.

EXCEPTIONAL LOADS

Greater or smaller student loads can be determined by educational consequence as well as schedule feasibility. This is suggested, of course, by the flexible schedule itself, where the number of courses that a student takes is no longer determined by the number of periods in the day. Once you start planning schedules with 30 and 40 and 50 per cent unscheduled time for students, then you can do a lot of adding to schedules and make some of them exceptionally heavy. We find students doing this regularly and extensively already. Let's crank into our mental processes the possibility that a student can absorb seven periods of class in a six-period day. Once we admit this possibility, we can examine the merit of exceptional loads in a way we haven't before. There's nothing immoral about giving a student double credit if he's bright enough to divide his time between two classes meeting at the same time. For the same reason there is nothing wrong with a student being allowed to take fewer subjects—or an unusual combination of courses that will make him more positive about school. Often "six classes in six periods" mentality comes from a fear of leaving a student on his own. Why shouldn't we?

VARIABLE CREDIT

Such credit could be predetermined. You might ask:
"Johnny, how would you like to take art for two units of credit instead of one? Or for a unit and a half credit?" Or perhaps you could say: "Johnny, go into the art class, and after you finish, we'll figure out how much credit you get." That shouldn't be so revolutionary, but it is. At one school using flexible scheduling with a very flexible and wonderful teacher, a student was sort of poking his nose in the art laboratory. She invited him in. In a minute he started looking longingly at a piece of clay, and she asked: "Want to make something?" And after he got it made, he wanted to know if he could fire it in the kiln. Then he glazed it and got it all done, and he said, "Can I get credit for this?"

Well, now, we can't give students credit for something that

they've already done! Books that are read over the summer don't count for book reports. But this teacher said: "O.K. That's about six weeks' worth of work. If you add such-and-such and such-and-such, you can have one credit in art."

What's wrong with variable credit? Why can't we say, instead of "You've failed," that "You only get six weeks' worth of credit," or "one semester of credit for a year"? This would be a primitive but tentative step toward the definition of badly needed performance criteria.

ROADBLOCK REMOVAL

Here the object is to define total procedures to minimize a student weakness. For example, we know that Johnny doesn't write very well—maybe we could allow him a report that is dictated rather than written. Lots of students have their own tape recorders. Why shouldn't a student dictate his report, if he'd rather—particularly if he has already demonstrated conclusively his lack of ability in writing. Another alternative would be to take a student who has a terrible time with grammar—who always comes out badly "in writing." You know in advance how he's going to do on an assigned written project, and you also know you can't remedy his grammar and spelling. Why clobber this student over the head again and again with failure? Wouldn't it be nice—think of the morale boost—to assign an English teacher to work with him on his report and edit it before it was turned in? Put the English teacher on his side.

PARTIAL PARTICIPATION

This is based on an agreed reduction in objectives and credit. You can say to a student: "O.K., instead of getting a full year's credit in junior English, if you only want a semester's credit, we'll work out which of the objectives you don't have to meet."

The temptation, of course, would be to do it in a standard way—to say: "Anyone who doesn't want to get a full unit of credit may skip these seven assignments." But then, you're right back to the same spot again. The point is to get individualization. Negotiate with the student. Ask him: "What would you like to leave out if we reduce the credit a little bit?" And let him tell you.

MULTIPLE TEACHER ASSIGNMENTS

Let more than one teacher help the same class or the same student. The arrangement can vary from consultation to complete multiple class participation. Everybody knows that different people can learn from different teachers in different ways. It can be very valuable to have a student sit in on the same presentation given by two different teachers. It's one way of getting at individualized instruction to say to Johhny: "All right. You'll listen to a discussion of positive and negative ions as explained by Miss Jones, and then listen to Mr. Smith make the presentation."

Or—you know from last year that Johnny barely got through ninth grade English. Your prediction is that he will fail tenth grade English this year. That means he may have to take tenth grade English over again. And because English is required every year for graduation, we finally wind up with some kids taking English 10, 11, and 12 as seniors. If that's a reasonable assumption, it may be a good idea to assign some students to *two* tenth grade classes simultaneously.

Let's have this as an option. If there are students who are having difficulty with a course, let them sign up twice for that course. And if you're concerned about credit, double the credit. We have credit to burn in schools—we are shorter on learning.

STUDENT SELECTION OF TEACHERS

This isn't profound or novel; in some schools it's done. For some students, we gain a motivational advantage if we say to them: "All right, pick your poison—Miss Smith, Miss Brown, or Mr. Jones."

Let students switch around if they want to. If I get tired of Mr. Jones, let me go in and be bored by Mr. Smith for a while. Maybe even keep track of how it goes—that's called research.

EXCEPTIONAL SEQUENCES

In some cases, we should be able to waive prerequisites. The results might surprise you. Professor McDonald and I did an experiment in programed learning at Stanford University some years ago that was terribly embarrassing.

We had a 32 frame programed learning program—a research game that was well written and a lot of fun to play. We knew we could control learning just the way we wanted to. Then we said, let's see how bad learning can get; let's have some students study this program—but not in a carefully coordinated, logical order. Logically we started out by telling them all the information they needed—the name of the game, the size of the board, the shape of the playing pieces, and the basic moves. But we shuffled these up for the test case and put them in random order. The first frame told the students when they had to do a forced capture. They didn't know the name of the game, the playing pieces, how to move, or anything else.

What were the results? They learned even better than with our logically developed program. I think it was quite presumptuous of the students to louse up our results that way. But there they were, defying the logical nature of the development of the curriculum. The elementary social studies curriculum is pretty much in the same boat. They start with the child, and no one can argue with that. Then they go to the neighborhood and the community and the state and the nation and our Western neighbors and the grand finale in the sixth grade is "our neighbors around the world."

The trouble is, my kindergartner has been to Puerto Rico and he hasn't been to the firehouse. The tight light logic of progression that we have is often nonsense. What confidence do we have that our prerequisites are the right ones? In some schools they are so silly as to define Art I as being art that is taken by a freshman or sophomore, and Art II as art taken by a junior or senior. What a wonderful performance criterion that is.

What do you suppose would happen if we allowed a student to take geometry before he had algebra? What might happen if a student took chemistry as a sophomore or a freshman, before he had the mathematics to cope with it? Maybe we could combine another technique of individualization and let one of the juniors or seniors tutor him in the math when he got stuck. When he got through as a senior, I wonder if this student would know less or more chemistry than if he had taken it the standard way as a junior.

We could even allow for the fact that this would make chemistry two years more remote from graduation—but that shouldn't bother us because after six to eight weeks the retention is down to about the 20 per cent level anyway, and it can't fall off much more than that.

Do you really know what would happen if you allowed freshmen to take the senior course in government? This needn't be assigned on a wholesale basis, but as a technique for individualizing or even to provide us with information on the real consequences of a particular set of prerequisites and their violation. What do you think would happen if we allowed kids to take two courses in the same sequence simultaneously? For example, algebra and geometry. I submit that if you let students take algebra and geometry together, not much would happen—at least for some students—except the teacher would be traumatized.

LATE ENTRIES OR DROPS

Why does everything have to start in September and end in June? Along about the 15th of November, why can't we collar a student or two, and say: "Let's throw away your program and plan a new one. You can change anything that you want. Now that you've seen things for half of a semester, what would you like to do differently?" Most students would be so aghast at the suggestion they wouldn't know how to deal with it. Likewise, if a student is doing poorly in a course in May, let him drop it. I'm not convinced we gain anything by putting failures on a transcript. A nonentry is eloquent testimony enough that he hasn't learned a course yet. Maybe there's a motivational tool here we haven't been using.

ROUTINE INCOMPLETES

Why not start a policy that would require the elimination of all borderline grades? Any time that a grade was on the borderline, the teacher can't give it. Instead of flipping a coin between a B— and a C+, the teacher should be required to get additional evidence. Have a tie-breaker.

Or have some sort of a standard incomplete option. Encourage students to depose the regimen with some agreed consequences. If a student says, "I don't think I'm done with this course," say, "O.K., you're not done; we'll give you an incomplete. You tell us what you're going to do to complete it and then we'll tell you what we'll do about the grade.

He'll say: "I need a B in this course, because it's a college course, and so far my grade is a C+." We say: "Fine, if you don't want a C+, we'll give you an incomplete instead. Now let's work out something that we can mutually agree will be a demonstration of sufficient competence to warrant the B."

SUBSTITUTE ASSIGNMENTS

Give students set performance criteria and allow them to select alternative instructional procedures to accommodate individual preferences. One reason educators didn't get to this notion earlier is because it is built squarely on performance criteria—knowing what the end is, knowing when we're done. One big problem of education right now is that we don't know when we're done. We have no way of knowing when a student is finished. If we could identify performance criteria, if we could pinpoint what an assignment is trying to accomplish, we would be able to substitute assignments routinely.

My experience as a teacher—and here I'm citing intuitive evidence, not research evidence—has always been that whenever I allow students to pick their own assignments, they usually pick more than I could assign them. That's part of this idea.

THE OPEN TRANSCRIPT

Why not revise performance reports the way you would the chapters in a book? Think of the transcript not as a document that is compiled in February and June, but as a document that reflects the current state of the student's knowledge or even just "high water mark" rather than the arbitrary designation of that knowledge. I study algebra for a while and I learn C's worth. If I want to come back and demonstrate later that the C's worth has changed to a B's worth, I can substitute B for C. Still later that B can be erased and made A. Any entry on the transcript would be considered temporary until the student left school. Who cares whether this happens in

September or February or May? It would be interesting to see if we doctored the transcript whether that would produce a more accurate prediction of college success than does the arbitrary transcript we now use.

LESSON ALTERNATIVES

Allow students to provide alternatives to the standard fare. The student says: "I know I'm not very good at literature—but could I write some extra poetry?" Or, a student says: "I hate to write short stories. Could I do an extra book report?"

THE TUTOR-COURSE OPTION

This will work when we have genuine performance criteria. Right now, in most schools, if you get an A in Language I, you can go on to Language II. If you get a B, you go on to Language II. If you get a C, or D, you go on to Language II. But with an F, you return to Lanuage I; no credit and you repeat the same course.

And yet we know that kids who get C and D in Language I are doomed to failure in Language. How do we defend an attrition rate in a language program that often reaches 90 per cent? Seems to me that we need to invent a Language $1\frac{1}{2}$, where students who get C and D have a chance to get their performance level up to an A or B in Language I. Then send them into Language II, and we can predict they will succeed. Once we get the performance criteria better established, the tutor-course option will become a much more significant part of the instruction and grading in the school.

WHEN SHOULD I INDIVIDUALIZE INSTRUCTION?

Don H. Parker

How can I individualize instruction? A better question would be "*When* should I individualize instruction?"

To answer this, let us first examine the total schooling process—the twelve years between the ages of six and seventeen or eighteen, during which we attempt to offer schooling for all the children of all the people.

Schooling includes two separate and distinct elements: *training* and *education*. *Training* is skill-getting. *Education* is skill-using. In the *education* part of schooling, the child uses basic skills gained in a systematic training situation to generate and use knowledge in a "project" or "unit of study" situation meaningful to him.

Traditional schooling consisted mainly of skill-getting and packing in knowledge. This was called "education," although it was really only training. This overattention to skill-getting and fact-packing led to a kind of schooling not appropriate for all of the children of all of the people. Many children were unable to relate what they learned to life. As learning became less and less meaningful, the child dropped out of school.

Then came the "progressive" movement, in which emphasis was on *use* of skills and knowledge in a lifelike situation. Around 1915, with the impact of Dewey's philosophy, schools began emphasizing education as an active, rather than passive, process; learning was experimentation instead of imitation.

Reprinted from *Grade Teacher* Magazine by permission of the publishers. Copyright April 1962 by Teachers Publishing Corporation.

Kilpatrick was to say that learning should involve purposeful activity and should begin with a problem that created interest and developed initiative.

Unfortunately, the progressive movement tended to throw the baby out with the bath. Skills and knowledge received less and less attention in favor of project work. "Skills," said the progressive, "would come as the child discovered a need for them." This was all very well, but progressive education failed to provide such skill-getting and knowledge-learning situations for the child when he was ready.

Nor was there any systematic track of reading, writing, and arithmetic skills except that laid out by the textbook. Teachers who did a good job on projects often did a poor job on skills and vice versa. Too often, the result was that neither was done very well. Sometimes the teacher simply focused on either skills or projects, to the neglect of the other, thus producing unbalanced schooling.

Do we have to settle for either/or? Can't we have both? We can if we have a basic track of skill-getting on the one hand, *and*, on the other, projects in which the child discovers the usefulness of his skills for successfully cooperating and competing in a group project. Equally important, the education part of schooling furnishes the situation in which he will discover the need for more knowledge.

We can now answer the question, "When should I individualize?" Answer: for the *training* part of the schooling process, individualization of instruction should be the rule when we want to help the child learn such basic skills as reading, writing, spelling, and arithmetic.

When should I "group"? Answer: for the *education* part of the schooling process. Here the goal is to give the pupil an opportunity to *use* the skills he has learned in a lifelike situation from which he can pull out his own meanings.

While it is possible to learn a skill—and much knowledge —in a relative vacuum, the *profitable use* of our skills comes only as a member of society. Somebody has to buy them.

Why not grouping for the learning of basic skills in the first place? Because in the group of six or eight or ten children, the group norm is so obvious that children will feel the need for an attempt to conform to it, whether they conform upward or downward. The best reader and the worst reader in a group so "stick out" that both are uncomfortable. From this standpoint, there is possibly more sense in trying to teach reading in a group of 35 than in a group of eight, since the "false norm" is spread thinner and therefore is less obvious. Grouping for instruction in skills, then, probably actually does more to inhibit learning than it does to help it.

Even more important, however, is the fact that in "grouped" instruction relatively little learning takes place because there is so little opportunity for *learning behavior* on the part of each child in the group. Few teachers can take the time to make sure that each of six, eight, or ten children learn each skill introduced during a twenty-minute reading session, for example.

As the year moves on, feelings that kill rather than build a learning situation soon develop. "What's the use?" says the slower learner. "They just run off and leave me." Equally tragic and wasteful is the case of the faster learner. "Why don't they hurry up? I finished a long time ago!"

A major fallacy in the "grouping-for-instruction" theory seems to be that it is somehow believed that *all* children in a group of six, eight, or ten are getting practice, while *one* child is doing the learning behavior. The fallacy here is that *watching* behavior and *doing* behavior are not the same.

Skill-getting is an internal, active, and a completely individual thing. It is not a matter of simply listening. It is a matter of doing something—of behaving. It requires not only taking in, but giving back.

The behavior required in learning one of the skills of reading, for example, is quite precise. The learner first meets the skill; learns what it is, what it does. Next, he engages in practice, or the attempt to perform the skill himself. During this practice he needs a feedback after each attempt. He needs to know whether he has "hit the mark" or whether, in his next attempt, he should "correct his aim" by different behavior. Gradually, he eliminates the wrong behavior and retains the right.

It takes no scientific training to understand that the behavior just described can only take place in the mind of the learner, that no one can do it for him.

This brings us to another important fact of life and reason why basic skill-getting must be a completely individualized learning opportunity: *Where two or more pupils participate in a learning situation, significant individual differences exist in both learning rate and capacity.* If maximum learning is to take place, it is necessary to provide a situation in which each child may start where *he* is and move ahead as *fast* and as *far* as his learning *rate* and *capacity* will let him.

By individualizing instruction in the basic skills, two important things are accomplished: (1) Pupils learn better and faster than they do in grouped instruction and (2) the teacher's time is saved for the more important work of being a learning consultant and/or a curriculum planner for each pupil.

"But," you say, "if I have trouble finding time to teach three groups in reading, for example, how can I possibly find time to teach all 29 of my pupils individually?" Answer: Shift your emphasis from teaching to *learning*. "Laboratory-ize" your instruction so that, after a major learning sequence is introduced, instruction is individualized and largely self-operating.

Individualizing instruction in this manner is not as difficult as it sounds. At present many teachers are using various kinds of workbooks, but they are often being used on a one-level basis or, at best, in two or three groupings. Why not use workbooks at several levels, giving the right workbook to the right child, according to his learning ability? Even better, and less expensive, break such materials down into even smaller "learning units" so the child gets the satisfaction of completing a job.

Further, many teachers spend long hours correcting the workbook responses. When they do this, they are actually robbing the child of a good half of his learning opportunity. Why not give the child responsibility for correcting his own work from a key, which can be prepared by the teacher and which children can soon become expert in using?

Still further, since children like to know (as do we all) "how am I doing?" why not devise a way so that the results can be recorded on some form of running record or progress chart? In this way, both pupil and teacher can get the "feel" of progress and some idea of where to look for the trouble, if progress is not being made.

With several instructional levels available, how will you know at what level each child should be working? The results of any good standardized test will be found helpful. Simply take the child's score and reduce it by *at least* one grade level (often two) to arrive at his functional level—the level at which he is able to work comfortably at that time. For example, if a pupil in the fifth grade shows a reading comprehension score of 4.5, he should be given material to work on at a beginning third grade level. The same would hold true for pupils testing above the level of the grade in which they are sitting. In the case of reading, an informal reading inventory can be a helpful supplement in questionable cases.

Self-programming, laboratory-type individualized instruction, as described above, has been worked out by teachers in reading at both primary and elementary levels. Similar work has also been done in spelling, some phases of writing, and in arithmetic. Materials used have been workbooks and textbooks disassembled and reassembled by hand into kits stationed about the room.

Regular laboratory periods are scheduled in each skill area, usually in the morning when minds are fresh. This is followed by unit or project work in late morning or afternoon, involving planning, generation of knowledge through reading, films,

TV, and so forth, and application of skills and knowledge in forwarding the group's project and the individual's part in it.

When children work in groups, should they be homogeneously or "ability" grouped—slower ones together, average in another group, superior in another, gifted in another, and so forth? There is much to recommend heterogeneous project groups—and the more heterogeneous the better.

For one thing, homogeneous grouping tends to set up a "caste system" which is not the best training for working toward the democracy we idealize. For another thing, there are enough varied activities in a well-planned project or unit to meet a wide range of ability levels.

This description corresponds much to the lifelike situation of a large research group in which there are the head scientists, the apprentice scientists, the technicians, the clerical workers, the tool makers, and finally the maintenance people who simply keep things clean and in order. As work gets underway, functional groups and subgroups will develop, ranging from two pupils to, at times, the entire class, with assigned "project groups" running around six, eight, or ten. Relating the roles of individuals from project to project can further broaden the learning experience of each pupil.

Thus, a group project, in itself, can afford a great amount of individualization or individualized learning opportunity, if the teacher will simply let it happen. The teacher's role in the education part of schooling is that of planning coordinator, resource person on locating needed knowledge, and consultant in evaluating learnings growing out of the project for each project group and for each individual. It is these all-important *education* activities for which the teacher's time should be saved—and can be saved when *training* activities are individualized.

What will be the end product for children in such a project situation? The product of each child, while different from that of his classmates, should represent *his* best work. Naturally, there will need to be a somewhat "standardized" type of product each pupil will be responsible for producing to demonstrate his grasp of the central theme of the topic, and to give meaningful practice in *using* the tool skills he is learning systematically in the training part of his school day. There should also be a unique product from each pupil—a drawing, a model, a "book," a role in a play, and so forth, that will stimulate creativity and deepen part-whole comprehension of the central theme.

In overview, we have considered the questions: *How* can I individualize and *when* should I individualize? We have seen that both individual and group instruction are desirable in the total schooling process. In the training part (skill-getting), individualized instruction is essential if learning is to take place as effectively as it can. In the education (skill-using and knowledge-generating) part of the schooling process, a combination of group planning, individual study, and group participation is usually most desirable.

Possibly one-half of a pupil's time would be spent in basic skill training. The other half of his time would be spent in project work in science and social studies. In the primary grades, a larger proportion of time would be devoted to training in skills; in upper elementary grades, more time would be devoted to the education part of schooling, as children become more ready and adept at planning and responsibility-taking. By recognizing the two separate elements of schooling, providing for both individualized and group learning situations, and concentrating on *learning* rather than on *teaching*, you can provide a balance in the two kinds of growth each of your pupils must experience: growth *as an individual* and *as a member of society*.

A CLIMATE FOR INDIVIDUALITY

Joint Statement of

AASA, ASCD, NASSP, DRE (NEA Departments)

Many schools and communities today are seeking to establish an educational climate that fosters individuality. To help them with this important task, the following questions should be useful. Positive answers to a majority of the questions will identify schools and school systems where individuality can thrive.

PHYSICAL FACILITIES

Is the building constructed so that room sizes can be changed easily?

Are the classrooms constructed so as to allow small groups to gather for learning or conferences?

Is provision made in classrooms, library, or elsewhere for pupils to work on individual assignments or to do independent research or study?

Are language laboratories available so that pupils may move at their own rate in different languages?

Do the science laboratories provide opportunity for individual effort and storage space for individual projects?

Does the school have rooms which can be used for indi-

Reprinted from *NEA Journal*, Vol. 55, November 1966, pp. 34–35, with the permission of the publisher.

vidual music or speech instruction, for individual or small-group listening to music, or for viewing motion pictures and slides?

Has space been provided for individualized sports, such as bowling and swimming, and for remedial work in body-building and posture?

Is there a place for relaxation and informal discussion?

Do teachers have access to an instructional center with such physical equipment as duplicators and a photographic dark-room?

ORGANIZATIONAL PATTERN

Do teachers have time at the beginning of the year for preplanning?

Do they have time during the year and at the end to complete records so that what they have learned about individuals will not be lost?

Do teachers' weekly schedules allow for pupil conferences?

Is the schedule flexible enough to allow for class periods to be expanded or contracted?

Does the program make a careful distinction between learning activities which can be carried out in large groups and those which need to take place on a small-group or individual basis?

Are pupil-teacher ratios low enough that a teacher can spend time with each pupil and consider each as an individual?

Do organizational patterns accommodate the continuous-growth concept of learning?

THE TEACHER

Does the teacher have a rich, varied, and creative pattern of experience?

Does he use the clues he finds in the cumulative records and in daily contacts as a basis for individualized assignments and projects?

Does he keep a written record of what he learns about each child? Does he assess its accuracy at intervals?

Is he tolerant of deviations in interests, values, intellectual specialties, creativeness, and competencies? Does he involve his pupils in cooperative planning to bring into the open individual goals, concerns, and aspirations as well as common needs and goals?

Does he provide his pupils with ways to achieve recognition and success?

Does he help his pupils to achieve self-perception, including realistic self-appraisal of strengths and weaknesses? Does he find ways to limit over-selfish ambition?

Does he create a general atmosphere of warmth in the classroom and make each child feel accepted and supported?

Does he inspire the kind of confidence that enables a child to bring into the open his hopes and his problems—personal as well as educational—without fear of recrimination or humiliation?

Does he encourage the free exchange of questions and ideas, the trying out of new experiences?

CURRICULUM

Is the educational program flexible enough to give the teacher considerable latitude in the selection of experiences appropriate for each learner?

Are the learning experiences organized so that pupils of varying abilities and interests can be assured of a reasonable amount of success?

Is the curricular pattern determined only after careful, consistent identification of differences in pupil characteristics, and subject to change when a change in emphasis and direction is indicated?

Is provision made for special programs for groups such as

the rapid learners and the gifted, the physically handicapped, the emotionally disturbed, and the mentally retarded?

Do courses of study, syllabi, and resource units contain suggestions for meeting the needs of individual learners, for self-testing devices, for pursuit of special interests and aptitudes, and for wide latitude in exploratory and creative experiences?

Are groupings kept flexible in terms of subjects, interests, and aptitudes?

INSTRUCTIONAL METHODS AND MATERIALS

Do the teaching methods stimulate the student to individual exploration and learning and lead him on to new and widely varied experiences?

Does the way of teaching help learning become a pleasant, exciting experience, leading to the development of a love of learning?

Do pupils feel encouraged to ask questions?

Does the method of teaching provide an active rather than a passive role for the learner?

Is the teaching organized to provide varied ways in which a pupil can be authentically successful? Does it stimulate responses at various levels of ability? Does it stretch the thinking of pupils at all levels?

Can the teaching be adapted to the most suitable method of approach—individualized, small group, or large group—to a given lesson?

Does the method of teaching increase individual responsibility and provide opportunities for each student to organize his own learning?

Does the teacher's way of working foster confidence and make pupils secure enough to try out creative ideas without undue fear?

Are instructional materials selected with an eye to their

adaptability for and encouragement of individual study and individual competence?

Is a wide variety of instructional materials available, suitable to divergent individual needs as well as to various levels of ability?

Are instructional materials selected to stimulate individual action—to give learning an active rather than passive character?

STATE AND FEDERAL GOVERNMENT

Do the state and federal governments give financial support to meet local needs?

Do they encourage and reward responsible local action?

Do they provide leadership for maximum individual development?

Do they discourage rigid conformity to standards?

LOCAL COMMUNITY

Are the power structures of the community—the social, political, religious, civic, economic, and fraternal organizations —objective in viewing diversity? Do they tend to accept, even welcome, differences?

Does the community provide a climate of support for ventures with a positive goal regardless of their outcome?

Does the community stimulate intellectual growth and provide a climate for lifetime learning?

BOARD OF EDUCATION

Does the board of education pursue personnel policies that encourage cooperation and diversity within the staff?

Does it help interpret to the community the value of diversity?

Does it encourage careful experimentation with new methods and materials?

Is it sensitive to the varied needs of youngsters and willing to back multiple means of serving them?

Is it receptive to budgets that contain an emphasis on resources for the individual as well as for the group?

Does it encourage provision of an abundance of stimuli for the inquiring minds of both youths and adults?

Does it provide the administration with support for individual staff and pupil development?

Is it receptive to modifying the existing organization and operation of the school when necessary for individualization of the curriculum?

Does the board itself relate to the administrators in a way which encourages comfortable administrator-staff relationships?

Do its policies allow teachers academic freedom to search continually for the truth?

PARENTS

Do parents encourage children to respond to the school's comprehensive and flexible program?

Do they try to understand the school program and give it positive support?

Do they encourage children to try new ideas at home?

Do they accept individuality within the community?

Do they give support to individuality and creativity in their own children and others?

Do they continue their own learning and individual development?

Do they value learning for its own sake?

Do they help their children understand themselves and their relationship to school and community?

This checklist has been abridged from *A Climate for Individuality* (1965. 56 pp. $2. Stock No. 021-00590) published by the American Association of School Administrators, Association for Supervision and Curriculum Development, National Association of Secondary-School Principals, and Department of Rural Education (NEA departments).

THE GENTLE ART
OF NON-TEACHING

Lee Lewin

Every faculty has its share of eager, inexperienced teachers who overwork, overworry, and underachieve. The old-timers, i.e., those who have mastered the gentle art of non-teaching (smile), nod knowingly and keep their secrets. The purpose of this article is to instill instant wisdom into the novice teacher, thus expanding effectiveness, which will benefit both the teacher and the students, while somewhat reducing the smugness of the old hands.

BASIC CONCEPTS

The first mistake most beginning teachers make is that of overteaching. Having been drilled in lesson-planning skills, the beginner spends endless hours writing detailed plans encompassing huge quantities of material to be taught through numerous enrichment activities. Usually, the students manage to do only half (or less) of what was planned. The teacher may decide at this point to omit parts of the plan, but this is frustrating in view of the time spent making them. Generally, the action taken is that the teacher clips along at her own pace, she gets through the lesson plan by doing all the work; the students are passive observers, and they get through the lesson too—relatively unaffected.

Reprinted from *Media & Methods*, Volume 5, February, 1969, by permission of the publisher.

Point One. Lesson Plans are assistants, not bosses!! If a portion of your plan exceeds allotted time, let it do so. Teach that thing well, and save the unused portion of your plan as a bank account. (The Gentle Art of Keeping Reserves.)

Another very common error made by new teachers is that of doing everything. The teacher knows the direction the lesson is to take, but students do not always comply. Time becomes a factor; there are pages to be covered, points to be made. The teacher starts a talkathon, which may include giving all the answers to the questions cited, but which does not include student participation; time for student digestion of information, and time for student expulsion of information to demonstrate what was absorbed. As one supervisor once told a teacher after observing a lesson, "You did a great job of teaching yourself, but I'm not sure what the students got out of it."

Point Two. Exposure does not equal teaching!! Just as watching a chef cook a meal does not appease the hunger of the observer, watching a teacher plunge through a lesson will not educate a student. It is the person involved in the processes of ingestion, digestion, and expulsion who has the benefit of absorption of knowledge. (The Gentle Art of Guiding Without Pushing-Pulling.)

ADVANCED CONCEPTS

Assuming that you accept the theory of utilizing lesson plans to the fullest, and that you are ready to let the students do the learning, you are now ready for an advanced concept in non-teaching, i.e., letting the students do the teaching!! Having realized that unskilled teaching is an exercise in self-clarification, you are in a position to use this awareness. This should not be attempted until you know which students grasp materials easily and which need closer observation. Once you know your students, try letting them teach each other in some of the following ways:

1. Pair them off for written work with the understanding that answers will be compared with a team only after each finishes the assignment. (Roam the room as arbiter in case of conflict, and to assist individuals having trouble with the work.) When most pairs have finished the work, let one pair lead the class in checking the assignment.

2. Relegate your routines to students (make certain you have established routines first!). Have one of the students hear answers to exercises. Let the student try to clear up misconceptions. If the student gets into trouble, let a student who does understand clarify for the class. (Don't let too much misinformation run rampant—pick your leader astutely, but not always the same person, please.)

3. Never answer even a casual question if it can be answered by a student.

4. Never do board work which can be done by a student—especially underlining, circling, writing corrections, and filling blanks.

5. Never resolve a conflict of opinion if research by the class can do so. Let them find their own answers.

6. Never tell information which can be located in a textbook, library book, or somewhere at that time in the classroom.

Point Three.   Keep mouth shut, body and mind in motion!! Sure, you know the answers, but the students have to learn them. Every time one student explains to another he is consolidating his own grasp of concepts. Besides, half the time students understand where their fellow students lost the point better than the teacher and can help each other more directly. (The Gentle Art of Doubling Student Participation Through Your Seeming Non-Participation.)

Lastly, the problem of satisfaction. For the new teacher this often comes (with appropriate uneasiness) solely from finishing the lesson plan. For the student, however, the greatest satisfaction comes from "getting it," really seeing what was being taught, and being able to use it. Unfortunately, students often cannot identify the "it" they are supposed to be learning. Too often students are motivated to feel achievement because they finished a long assignment, because they pleased the teacher, because they got the highest grade, finished first, had the prettiest paper, or (worst of all) had the longest paper. Now, the teacher knows that competitiveness, wordiness, and unctuous compliance are not the aim of the lesson, thus the students' misdirected efforts are a source of guilt. A principled teacher wants to do more than "get through." Students who are able to use what they've learned are able to demonstrate that to the teacher and themselves. The glow of "I've got it!" on a student's face spells satisfaction for him—and for the teacher . . . and it's the kind of satisfaction that bears no burden of uneasiness.

Point Four.   Keep no secrets from your students!! Tell them what you are teaching, and how. During the lesson and at the end of each lesson have the students tell you what they are studying, why, and how. (The Gentle Art of Setting the Objective in Order to Achieve It.)

SUMMARY

By following this brief guide to non-teaching, the novice avoids overwork, practices self-preservation, becomes free to roam the room for those who need the most help, moves around to see what's really happening at each desk, avoids guilt over not doing the right job, avoids anxiety over the students not getting the right learning, and has a legitimate sense of achievement . . . after all, when you grade yourself, the grade counts more than ever before!

DO WE GROUP IN AN INDIVIDUALIZED PROGRAM?

Dorris M. Lee[*]

"Hi, Bill! Did you see the notice on the bulletin board? Jim and Kathy are going to discuss Jean Lee Latham's book, *Carry On Mr. Bowditch*,[1] this morning about 10 o'clock. You wanted to find out about how sailors use sea charts and maps. Let's join the group."

And at 10:05 five boys and three girls join Jim and Kathy in the story-sharing corner of the room. Jim starts by giving the setting and general focus, with an introduction of the main characters and the part they play in the story. Kathy develops the main theme and gives some personal reactions to the author's style and the feeling of reality she has about the characters. Then Jim explains what he has learned about using charts and maps at sea, which is what Bill has joined the group to hear. He begins asking Jim questions about it. Others join in, some with questions, some with comments, and two of them suggest further sources they have found helpful. Kathy then comments on what she has found about Jean Lee Latham's background on this topic and her other biographies. At this point some of the group begins to drift away and back to activities with which they are now more vitally concerned.

[*] Written with encouragement and suggestions from teachers (grades 1 through 8) Mary Crawford, Beaverton; Florence Edwards, David Douglas School District, Portland; Elizabeth Gill, Vancouver, Washington; Carole Lisignoli, Portland; Joseph Rubin, Portland; Lynn Rystogi, Portland; Donna Sposito, Portland.

From *Childhood Education*, Vol. 45, No. 4 (December 1968), pp. 197–199. Reprinted by permission of Dorris M. Lee and the Association for Childhood Education International, 3615 Wisconsin Avenue, N.W. Washington, D.C. Copyright © 1968 by the Association.

[1] Jean Lee Latham, *Carry On, Mr. Bowditch* (Boston: Houghton Mifflin Company, 1955).

Of course there is grouping in an individualized program! The groups are just formed differently, for different purposes, and continue for different lengths of time. But first we must make clear what we consider individualized instruction to be. *Since* a learning situation, to be effective, must be such that each child can bring personal meaning to it, the child must have at least a part in the planning and decision-making. *Since* each learns in his own way and from the framework of his own present understandings, each must have a part in determining his own procedures for learning. Thus individualized instruction on necessity must involve self-directed learning.

Self-directed learning is a far cry from the justly feared do-whatever-you-want variety. Here the learner identifies his own educational needs, decides what he can do to meet them and how he can most effectively carry out his purposes. The teacher may help as little as by raising a question or as much as by extended conferencing. Planning with children helps them learn how to identify needs and procedures in terms of purposes. Individual conferences, in which the teacher can talk with each child about how he can identify needed learnings and how he decides what procedures would meet his purposes, are most useful in developing self-direction.

WHAT IS A GROUP?

In this context, what is a group? It is those children who at that time have common specific concerns, needs, interests, or plans. It may be initiated by one or more of the children involved or by the teacher or by the interaction of teacher and children. The group stays together as long as the specific reason for its establishment still exists. Some children may leave and others join as their immediate needs are met or developed.

Groups in which children have a part in deciding their

participation or which grow out of self-directed activity have values that do not accrue from teacher-established and maintained groups. Almost by definition, there is involvement and purpose not otherwise possible. This eagerness and single-mindedness develop unique learnings. Self-selection of an individual or group learning activity brings commitment attained in no other way. The child then feels a responsibility to himself or the group.

Mr. Swanson finds that Suzy, Bob, Karen, and Billy have difficulty recognizing base words in derived words. Each one also has become aware that he has not yet learned this, mainly through his or her individual conference with Mr. Swanson. So the group is formed to work together with the teacher in clarifying the problem, each suggesting ways of solving it from his own perceptions and reactions. One child after another gains insight, feels he understands, and leaves the group. With only Bob left, the teacher explores *his* thoughts and perceptions related to base and derived words. He discovers that he has always thought "base" meant "bottom" and never really has been able to bring any meaning to the word in this context. Each time he has thought he understood from the examples, he has become confused by the term. Mr. Swanson clears the meaning and Bob moves another step forward.

PURPOSES FOR GROUPING

Individuals are unique, and while broadly speaking most have common general needs, immediate and specific needs and concerns differ widely. We believe content is primarily for use in developing concepts and understandings about the the world of people and things in which the child lives. Further, we believe that a great variety of content may be used to develop needed concepts and understandings. Since children learn most effectively when dealing with material and ideas to which they can bring personal meaning, they will be using a wide variety of content. The number identifying with certain specific content at any one time may vary from one to possibly eight or ten. If the whole group has had a particularly meaningful experience, they may all want to discuss and think together for a while at least. Groups then provide a vehicle whereby those who can relate well to certain content or ideas may work together in a way most meaningful to them.

A sixth-grade class has been having a variety of experiences that have oriented them to South America's problems, weaknesses, strengths, and concerns; to its climates and general geography; to the languages of its people. Their familiarity with names of countries has alerted the children to comments relevant to South American situations in newspapers and magazines, on TV and radio, and by parents and friends. One morning Sarah comes in with a clipping relating the concern of American meat packers to the importation of Argentine beef. She asked her mother about it and in the store that afternoon they checked the canned meat shelves in their grocery store. Now she wants to know more about it. Her questions and concerns attract several others and a group of six expresses interest in finding out what it means to cattlemen both in the United States and Argentina. Since the teacher believes that a study in depth of one or two countries provides more real understanding, as well as develops skills in tackling a problem to find answers, she encourages the group to go ahead. She also recognizes that such exploration leads into virtually every aspect of a country's life—economic, political, geographical, historical.

Another purpose for grouping may be to attain needed skills not developed in other ways. When children live in a fluid, exciting learning environment where eager, purposeful activity is ever present, most acquire many such skills as natural, untaught learnings. However, some needed skills may be missed. When this is noted, by teacher or children, those who need the skills will join a group for the purpose of acquiring them, so that they may more easily go on with what they feel they need and want to do.

A fourth grade has been working independently and in small groups to find out the various ways animals are useful to man and how man has affected the animals. They have been doing much reading and discussing and thinking, even copying out of books everything that has any relationship to the study, but some of the children are getting bogged down. Judy and Linda come to Miss Jenkins with the problem. Upon questioning the group, Miss Jenkins learns that ten of them are having trouble with notetaking. Although considerable attention was given to notetaking earlier in the year, this group knows they have not mastered the skill to the point of using it effectively.

Miss Jenkins suggests they, and any others who wish, meet that afternoon to pinpoint their problems. Twelve come to the meeting; specific problems are shared and ideas exchanged. Miss Jenkins gets them to think about their real purpose in taking notes, what they are going to use them for, how they can decide what to take down. After working for twenty minutes, they agree to try out their new understanding the next day and to meet together again on the following day to share progress, to ask further questions, and to check their skills by reading some of their notes to the group.

Groups form, shift membership, and dissolve more or less continuously on the basis of common interest. Sometimes they are instigated by the teacher, but more often in a self-directed classroom they develop spontaneously. Such groups may be for a wide variety of purposes and involve a wide variety of activities. Some of them are:

to work together in writing a story that may be presented to the class or taped for other groups to listen to and evaluate

to prepare for the reading of a play of their own, or one already written, for presentation to their class or another in the school

to preview and evaluate a film for use of a larger group or the entire class

to carry out the various functions necessary to the writing and "publishing" of a class or school newspaper

to decide on significant and challenging questions to pose to a larger group or class for the purpose of stimulating involved discussion dealing with the understanding of main issues in an area of learning

to use a listening post with tapes either teacher, child, or group made for any of a variety of purposes to watch film loops, filmstrips, or film and record combinations also for a variety of self-identified purposes

to solve problems of the moment, as when one or two children say, "We need to discuss this with everybody working on our project" or ". . . with everybody playing baseball at noon" or ". . . with those who want to plan what we need to think about when we write stories for first-graders to read."

SELF-DIRECTED GROUP WORK IN THE ELEMENTARY SCHOOL

Edmund Amidon and Ned A. Flanders

In the modern elementary school, teaching with groups is a much used approach to teaching all school subjects. Most primary teachers, for example, group their children for reading. Many elementary teachers use groups for teaching social studies, arithmetic, and science. They also encourage children to play or work informally on projects in groups. In many of the groups used in the elementary schools the teacher is the leader. The survey presented her, however, is concerned not with teacher-directed group work, but rather with self-directed group work. In the self-directed group the teacher is not dominant; that is, he is not the group leader. Rather, he acts as a guide or resource person.

There is very little published research concerning when and how self-directed group work can be introduced into the elementary and primary grades. Noar (3),[1] Thelen (4), and Flanders (1) have all discussed group work in the classroom and have presented principles and ideas which are useful for teachers attempting to work with classroom groups. Perhaps the most extensive study concerned with the development of children's groups can be found in Moreno's book, *Who Shall Survive?* (2), Moreno concludes p. 64, that older children

From *Elementary English*, Vol. 40 (April 1963), pp. 373–378. Reprinted with the permission of the National Council of Teachers of English and Edmund Amidon and Ned A Flanders.

[1] Numbers in parentheses refer to references at end of chapter.

can work together toward goals without adult supervision with increasing effectiveness, but that children younger than age eight or nine are probably immature for self-directed group work.

The major purpose of this article is to report the results of a series of interviews with teachers who are considered successful in using self-directed group work in their classrooms. The study is not experimental but is an informal survey of current practice. Information about how group work can be organized and carried out at different age levels was obtained from teachers who could speak from their own experiences. Some of their experiences run contrary to Moreno's conclusion.

PROCEDURE

All the teachers selected for interviews were considered by their supervisors to be successful in the use of group work. The forty selected were from a large, urban, mid-western school system; five were first-grade teachers, five were second-grade teachers, six were third-grade teachers, six were fourth-grade teachers, seven were fifth-grade teachers, and eleven were sixth-grade teachers.

Each teacher was interviewed separately, using a standardized interview situation. The interview consisted of open-end type questions designed to obtain as much information as possible about the group work of each teacher. Before asking questions, the interviewer defined self-directed group work. The following definition of group work was read to each teacher:

The teacher is not dominant in the group and is not the group leader; rather, he is a guide or resource person. Pupil leadership exists, either formal and recognized, or informal and officially unrecognized. The group has a goal which is clear and acceptable to its members. It will presumably be productive and will engage in some type of self-evaluative process; however, in the primary grades the latter process may be primarily teacher-directed.

The teachers were asked to respond to nine questions, keeping the foregoing in mind. They were encouraged to talk about each question so that as much information as possible could be obtained without restrictions. An example of how they used this freedom can be found in the way they answered the first question—"What is the lowest grade level at which self-directed group work can be successful?" In answering this question, teachers generally described what they felt to be the characteristics of successful group work at a particular grade level. The answers to each question were written on a standard form by the interviewer.

RESULTS OF INTERVIEWS

1. *What is the lowest grade level at which self-directed group work is possible?*

Teachers' answers to this first question seemed to be related to the grade level at which they were teaching. First-grade teachers indicated that first grade was the lowest grade for group work; second-grade teachers indicated that first and second grades were the lowest grades; third-grade teachers thought that second and third were the lowest grades for group work; fourth-grade teachers thought that third and fourth grades were the lowest; and fifth-grade teachers thought that fourth and fifth were the lowest grades. In spite of this trend, a majority of sixth-grade teachers still thought that group work was possible as early as the first grade. In discussing this first question, teachers who indicated that group work was possible in the primary grades explained that the type of group work in the early grades differs from that in the intermediate grades. They thought that goals, communication, productivity, and length of meetings must be very limited in the primary grades but could be gradually expanded as the grade level increased. On the basis of answers to this question it was evident that these teachers thought that between second and fourth grades a change in the type of group work does occur. The kind of group work in the early grades seems to center around an art or construction project. In the third or fourth grade a kind of group work emerges which lends itself more to intellectual and oral activity and less to motor activity.

2. *What are the most important factors in determining whether or not a teacher uses group work in his classroom?*

The teachers listed factors that are likely to be considered before initiating group work in the classroom, such as time available, subject studied, group readiness, class size, pupil age, and presence of discipline problems. Although most of the teachers interviewed in this study thought that these factors were all important, class size and time available were two in particular that were mentioned as possible deterrents to a teacher's use of group work. Some teachers said that the only case in which the factors mentioned could prevent a teacher from using group work would be if the class were much too large for the room or if time were tightly scheduled by the administration. Other teachers suggested that limited space and tight schedules might not prevent all group work but would certainly limit the amount of group work possible.

3. *How can a teacher prepare his class for group work?*

A variety of methods for preparing students for group work were listed by the teachers. The most frequently mentioned technique, listed by more than half of the teachers, was that of informal class discussion. The second most popular technique was the use of visual aids or similar types of motivating devices. The setting up of very specific and concrete goals for each lesson was yet another method of preparation. According to some teachers, demonstration of criteria for group leadership and group membership by means of a role-playing situation could be used to foster readiness for group work. A small group conducts a meeting before a class in which they show how a group can hold an orderly and productive meeting. This involves the demonstration of simple leadership and general discussion skills.

4. *How can a teacher tell when her class is ready for group work?*

One major problem that teachers face in planning for group work is that of determining when the class is *ready* to engage in group work. Most of the teachers indicated that the best way to determine the readiness for class group work was to attempt some limited and informal group projects and evaluate their success. Many teachers interviewed indicated that the children were ready for group work when they had learned to "work well independently." Children are ready for group work, according to other teachers, when they begin to show an interest in groups, when the teacher has developed good rapport with the class, and when the members of the class have become fairly well acquainted. A few teachers stated that they had merely observed the children at play and in informal groups to determine readiness. There was substantial agreement by these teachers, too, that the teacher must be willing to initiate group work in her class. Thus the readiness of the teacher is introduced as still another factor in determining when a class is ready for group work.

5. *What techniques do teachers use to divide their classes into small groups?*

The techniques used by teachers to divide their classes into groups were: interest in a topic, sociometric choice, and some form of arbitrary division accomplished by the teacher. In each case most teachers felt that the way the groups were formed depended on the purpose of the group activity.

Most of the teachers advocated letting the children choose their groups on the basis of interest in a topic. On the other hand, most teachers felt that children should work with children they liked. Many stated, therefore, that often both interest in topics and sociometric preferences enter into the formation of groups. For example, pupils often choose topics in which they are interested and then attract their friends to a certain group. They sometimes reverse the process and become interested in a topic of a particular group because of a friend in that group. Instances were also cited in which working with another pupil caused friendship to develop. Teacher direction was used when it seemed necessary to form more balanced groups in terms of ability and skill.

Some differences in responses among the grade levels were noted in reference to techniques for dividing the class. Only one teacher in first and one in second grade mentioned sociometric choice as a method. Most teachers felt that the sociometric techniques were less valuable with younger children than with older children.

6. *What is the role of the teacher in group work in the classroom?*

A large majority of teachers believed that the teacher should guide the planning sessions by setting limits within which the class can function. Other roles mentioned for the teacher in planning were to act as an encourager, to set up long-range goals for the class, to act as a resource person, and to set up very specific goals for the class. Several teachers made a distinction between letting the class have genuine freedom to plan its activities within the limits established and merely justifying the plans that the teacher has already determined.

7. *What effect do discipline problems have on the success or failure of group work in the elementary classroom?*

Teachers answered the discipline question in two basically different ways. First, there were a large number of teachers who felt that if a teacher had a number of discipline problems in class, it would restrict his use of group work, at least so far as these problem children were concerned. The other answer was that the presence of discipline problems would not only fail to restrict group work, but that group work would be the best method for handling discipline problems in many cases. The first answer was given primarily by teachers of the intermediate grades. The second answer was given more often by teachers of the primary grades.

8. *What subjects lend themselves best to self-directed group work?*

Almost all teachers interviewed said that social studies lends itself to group work more readily than does any other subject. Generally science was a second subject considered suitable for group work by many of the teachers from the first through the sixth grades. The third most frequently mentioned was art. In this subject, however, there was a grade level difference, as all but three of the teachers naming art as a good subject to teach in groups were in the primary grades.

Several teachers also mentioned the possibility of using self-directed groups in reading, as an enrichment activity. Several teachers seemed to feel that there were times when any subject can be taught successfully in groups. Most teachers interviewed apparently felt that while small groups can be used in teaching many subjects, there are some subjects that lend themselves to group work better than others.

At the lower grade levels many teachers combined art and social studies very successfully. At the upper grade levels most group work was done in the subjects of social studies and science. Since several teachers testified to the success of group work in all areas, it is probable that with experience in group method teachers extend the method to almost all areas of the curriculum at times.

9. *What are the advantages and disadvantages of group work?*

According to half of the teachers interviewed, the major advantage of group work is that it helps to develop the ability to get along with others. Some teachers named as major advantages those of maximum pupil participation and interest generated in children. Significant also is the suggestion by some of the teachers that group work develops in children the ability to work independently, as well as co-operatively. In addition, it helps to provide for individual differences.

IMPLICATIONS

Before summarizing the survey results, certain values about self-directed group work held by the authors should be made explicit. The first value is that some form of self-directed group work is desirable in the elementary school curriculum. This value stems from the belief that, taken altogether, classroom activities must permit children to develop those social skills that are required for self-control and self-discipline as well as provide for the development of the usual intellectual skills. The second value is that some form of self-directed group work can be carried out at any elementary grade level. First- and second-grade group work may be more properly described as developing readiness for group work; nevertheless group work at the primary level does exist. The third value is that self-directed group work brings into focus, more clearly than any other method of classroom instruction, the factors that affect the development of individual creativity and independence. In short, these values support the position that self-directed group work permits children to practice self-control, to set their own unique goals, to try their own problem-solving procedures, and to learn how to coordinate their actions with those of others.

The first major conclusion for this survey is that teachers employ self-directed group activities when *they* are ready. The teachers interviewed were already using self-directed group work successfully. They ranged from the first to the sixth grade. It is clear that the maturity of the children over this age range was an unimportant factor because if it were, we would find self-directed group work limited to some minimum age. Teachers in the classroom apparently disagree with Moreno's suggested minimum age.

Further evidence supporting the notion that group work occurs when the teacher is ready can be inferred from the answers to two additional questions. When teachers are asked how they can tell when their students are ready, their answers boil down to almost simple trial and error. The best way to tell if the children are ready is to try it. Organize one group, give that group lots of help, and see if the students are successful. The second bit of evidence results from the question about discipline. Here teachers' opinions are split, depending on their philosophy about group work: self-directed groups are used because discipline problems can be handled more effectively, contrasted with the idea that groups are used in spite of discipline problems. Apparently some teachers who are using group work successfully see it as a reward to be given to qualified students—those who have a maximum of self-control already at hand. Others see group work as an activity in which the initial steps toward self-control can be taken. One gets the impression that *the real issue is the teacher's tolerance for group breakdown and perhaps his skill at diagnosing and repairing group difficulties that can and frequently do occur.*

The second conclusion is a kind of corollary to the first. *No systematic procedures are commonly used to initiate and maintain self-directed group work.* Instead, teachers who are successful with group work report that they improvise and experiment with methods of clarifying goals, dividing the class, and deciding on their own role. This suggests that when a teacher is ready, he will find a way. This conclusion does not necessarily underestimate the importance of having some clear-cut procedures in mind on the first attempt, but it does suggest that subsequent experiences may be quite different and that the exact methods used on any single occasion are relatively unimportant.

Third, it can be reported that *teachers do not agree completely on which subject areas are best adapted to self-directed group work.* It is true that most teachers work in the area of social studies at first, but science and art are also mentioned. This finding is not surprising in view of the fact that the activity projects of self-directed groups have the specific advantage of integrating what otherwise might become a compartmentalized elementary program. Elementary children have always learned from teachers how to separate the various subject matter areas; children have no reservations about illustrating their social studies or science with art work, to see the social consequences of scientific experimentation and to integrate spelling, penmanship, music, and any other subject into a unified activity.

Finally, tucked away in the reactions of several insightful teachers is the opinion that *self-directed group work modifies the basic dependence on authority figures that develops in children.* They indicated their desire to develop interdependence, a balance between independent and dependent tendencies. One might assert that a gifted teacher can modify the strong dependent tendencies of children without recourse to self-directed group work, but these teachers felt they could develop more constructive interdependence among more children through successful, self-directed group work. As children mature and have ideas of their own, they must have opportunities to practice initiating action based on their own convictions. A number of teachers at various grade levels in this survey expressed ideas similar to these.

No conclusions can be reported from this survey concerning the general incidence of group work in a random sample of elementary teachers. Our sample included only teachers who were already known for their successful use of group methods. The major conclusion of this survey would be that if one wished to increase the general use of self-directed group work among elementary teachers, *the place to begin would be with the attitudes and opinions of teachers.* Once these are favorable, experimentation and exploration of group methods of teaching can start.

References

1. FLANDERS, NED A., *Teaching with Groups*. Minneapolis: Burgess Publishing Co., 1954, pp. 1–40.
2. MORENO, JACOB L., *Who Shall Survive?* Washington, D.C.: Nervous and Mental Disease Publishing Company, 1934, pp. 1–431.

3. NOAR, GERTRUDE, *Freedom to Live and Learn*. Philadelphia: Franklin Publishing and Supply Company, 1948, pp. 1–200.

4. THELEN, HERBERT A., "Group Dynamics in Instruction: Principle of Least Group Size." *The School Review*, 57 (March 1949), 139–148.

INDEPENDENT STUDY AS AN INSTRUCTIONAL TOOL

E. Paul Torrance

Most of us have sensed the truth in Thoreau's contention that some individuals "hear a different drum beat" and should step to this beat. Or we may have chuckled knowingly to M. M. Osborne's story of *Ondine*—a bird that could not learn under her parents' patient instruction but could, given time on her own, learn so successfully that she "just flew, or fished, or ran better than any of them." [1] We have recognized intuitively that Thoreau wrote the truth and that every classroom has its Ondines, yet we have looked upon the cases of independent learning as miraculous, not accepting the fact that independent study might be used deliberately as a powerful tool of learning.

Although there has been no systematic research of the potential of independent study as an instructional tool, experimental research has occasionally though accidentally, revealed evidence of its value and suggested that far more of it goes on than we realize. A study by McConnell [2] of the teaching of second-grade arithmetic by authoritative identification

Reprinted from *Theory Into Practice*, Vol. 5 (December 1966), pp. 217–221, with the permission of the author and the publisher.

[1] M. M. Osborne, Jr., *Ondine: The Story of a Bird Who Was Different*. Boston: Houghton Mifflin Company, 1960.

[2] T. Raymond McConnell, "Discovery vs. Authoritative Identification in the Learning of Children," *University of Iowa Studies in Education*, September 15, 1934, *9*, 12–62.

as opposed to the discovery method suggests that many children use independent study "in defense of themselves." McConnell was puzzled by some of his findings and interviewed the children in this large-scale study. Learning by authoritative identification has not been congenial to some of them, so they had used experimentation, manipulation, and other means and learned much through discovery. Similarly, because learning by discovery had not been congenial to others, some children had sought authorities outside the classroom for correct solutions. A close look at the data from almost any educational experiment, no matter how successful the experimental treatment, will show that some individuals failed to learn under the experimental condition and that some learned more on their own than the average learner under the experimental condition. There seems to be no method of teaching that is successful with all children who are capable of learning. In fact, a method that is quite successful with most children of average and below-average learning ability may be quite unsuccessful with a child of exceptionally superior learning ability.

WHY CONSIDER INDEPENDENT STUDY?

Teachers might well ask, "Why should I consider independent study a valuable tool of instruction? Wouldn't it be better to continue teaching the class as a group and let the independent study take place outside the classroom?" While teachers who deliberately use individual study as an instructional tool will be pioneering, a lot of research shows indirectly that they will not be taking too great a risk. Much educational research indicates quite clearly that some learners from nursery school to graduate school require a great deal more structure than others. The preference for open-structure learning situations and independent study seems more closely related to creative or divergent thinking ability than to intelligence as measured by present-day tests.[3, 4, 5, 6]

Extremely important in considering independent study is the growing realization that one of education's most important objectives is to give students the motivation and skill for life-long learning. The knowledge explosion and the increasing rate of change make it impossible for children to acquire in school all of the knowledge and skill they will need during their lives. Since much continued learning is likely to be through independent study, such study should be the most powerful instructional tool in helping young people acquire the motivation and skill for continued learning. And since one is more likely to use skills that have been practiced, the skills of independent study should be practiced from an early age.

WHAT CAN IT DO?

Let us examine more specifically what we can expect independent study to do, recognizing that we do not yet know

[3] E. Paul Torrance, "Different Ways of Learning for Different Kinds of Children" in *Mental Health and Achievement*, E. Paul Torrance and Robert D. Strom, editors. New York: John Wiley & Sons, Inc., 1965, pp. 253–62.

[4] James B. MacDonald, and James D. Raths, "Should We Group by Creative Abilities?" *Elementary School Journal*, December 1964, 65, 137–42.

[5] Nancy W. Clark, "A Study of the Relationship of Creativity, Preference for Open-Structure Learning Experiences, and Teacher Likes for Pupils in Grades 3–6," Master's thesis, Cornell University, 1964.

[6] Maxine S. Hamburg, "A Study of the Relationship of Creativity, Preference for Open-Structure Learning Experiences, and Teacher Likes of Children in Grades 3–6 of a New York City Elementary School," Master's thesis, Cornell University, 1964.

all of its possibilities. From the many recorded incidents that occurred more or less accidentally, we know that independent study can be used to solve certain kinds of problems. Severe behavior problems have disappeared when children have been allowed to study independently. Nonreaders have become good readers; nonachievers have become outstanding achievers; social isolates and rejectees have become accepted, productive group members; and apathetic, reluctant learners have become eager and excited about learning. Independent study is an ideal tool of instruction from the standpoint of motivation, for it both heightens children's natural curiosity and capitalizes on the motivation that comes from curiosity by challenging them to dig deeper and get beneath the superficial. It can provide an outlet for those who need to "sing in their own key" or "build sandcastles."

WHAT CAN'T IT DO?

Independent study creates certain very real problems and fears. It precludes keeping the curriculum the same for all children in a given classroom or grade level, thus creating problems in testing, grading, and accrediting work done. Since some learners require a great deal of structure, they may waste the time allotted for independent study or become extremely frustrated and give up efforts to learn. While independent study may be useful to all learners to some extent, it will be far more useful to some than to others. And it should probably not be the exclusive method of learning for any single learner.

It may seem, at this point, that employing independent study in our schools would reduce the need for teachers. Nothing could be further from the truth. The successful use of independent study requires the greatest repertoire of high-order teaching skills of any method of instruction. It requires the most sensitive and alert guidance, plus imagination, empathy, and a broad range of information. It also requires the ability

to help each child find each honest effort to learn rewarding enough to stimulate continued effort. Such teaching takes a great deal more intellectual and emotional energy than more traditional ways of teaching.

HOW DOES IT RELATE?

Since every teacher teaches differently, one cannot prescribe precisely the relationship between independent study and other parts of the program. Independent study may emerge naturally from the rest of the program, or the rest of the program could be determined by an analysis and synthesis of the common needs and interests of all the members of the classroom group that emerge through it. Letting independent study emerge from the rest of the program would probably enable the teacher to maintain better control and to carry out better planned sequences of learning experiences that would meet the common, predictable needs. Most teachers would probably feel more comfortable with a relatively standardized basic program supplemented by independent study. This plan should work successfully if the teacher will let one thing lead to another and take advantage of those unusual moments of learning readiness. In the teacher guides for some of the instructional materials my associates and I have developed, we have tried to alert users to some of these moments and provide suggestions to capitalize on them.[7]

WHAT PROFESSIONAL SKILLS DOES IT REQUIRE?

The successful use of independent study as an instructional tool requires professional skills presently beyond the scope

[7] B. F. Cunningham, and E. Paul Torrance, *Teacher's Guides for Image/Craft Material*. Boston: Ginn and Company, 1965.

of most teachers. Few teachers have engaged in independent study during their formal education, and the skills for such study are rarely taught in teacher education programs. In fact, there has been no systematic and rigorous determination of just what these skills are. On the basis of my own experiences in directing independent study among children and graduate students, I will briefly identify necessary skills and outline alternative plans for teachers to acquire them.

1. Recognize and Acknowledge Potentialities.   Teachers cannot provide opportunities for independent study unless they can recognize and acknowledge the learner's potentialities. Even if they have this ability, their attempts will rarely be more successful than chance. The recognition must be accurate and the acknowledgement sincere. Various standardized tests of mental functioning, motivation, and interest can help teachers recognize potentialities otherwise overlooked. Teachers should know how to use these tests, but they should never become dependent on tests alone.

2. Respect Students' Questions and Ideas.   Learners' questions and ideas are the real keys for activating independent study. If teachers ignore, ridicule, or otherwise derogate these questions and ideas, they will miss great opportunities for inspiring and guiding independent learning. Observations of classroom behavior and incidents recorded by teachers indicate that few teachers now have the skill to respect students' questions and ideas and that it is difficult, but not impossible, to improve this skill.[8]

3. Ask Provocative Questions.   It is not the question that calls for the reproduction of what is in the textbook, but the provocative question that stimulates creative thinking in a different way about what is known or confronts the learner

[8] E. Paul Torrance, *Rewarding Creative Behavior.* Englewood Cliffs, N.J.: Prentice-Hall, Inc., 1965.

with gaps in knowledge that sets the student off on independent study. Since several investigations reveal that over 90 per cent of the questions asked in classrooms call only for reproduction of textbook material or what the teacher has said, this is definitely a skill that needs to be improved and practiced.

4. Recognize and Value Originality. Recognizing and valuing the original ideas and productions of students should inspire and guide independent study. When anyone discovers something new to him, he wants and needs to communicate this to someone. The teacher who would mine some of the potential value of independent study should provide chances for this.

5. Develop the Ability to Elaborate. Much independent study involves the elaboration of an idea; this elaboration requires that one be able to keep an open mind, to see things in great depth, and to fill in the gaps in knowledge by imagination or the acquisition of more information.

6. Do Not Evaluate Practice and Experimentation. Students are often afraid to seek new information, develop new methods, or depart from prescribed requirements because they are afraid of making errors that will be held against them. Teachers, on the other hand, find it difficult to use unevaluated practice because they are accustomed to correcting students' work and have no other way of communicating with students about their work.

7. Develop Creative Readers. Independent reading should be done creatively rather than for reproduction. Something read creatively is always more likely to be remembered and used than something read with an absorbent or critical set. Creative reading involves heightening anticipation and expectation about what is read and using what is learned afterwards.

8. Predict Behavior Accurately. To provide the sensitive and alert guidance required in using independent study as an instructional tool, the teacher needs the skills of accurate observation and prediction of behavior.

9. Employ Planned, Guided Experiences. In using independent study, teachers will find that students will want to learn and use many concepts and skills before they are usually taught. Many of these concepts and skills can be mastered before they are traditionally taught if students are given a well-planned, guided sequence of experiences. Most teachers will need to learn the skills of creating such experiences and increasing student motivation to participate in them.

10. Develop Concepts and Skills of Research. In order not to be shallow and unproductive, independent study often requires the concepts and skills of historical, descriptive, and experimental research. Fortunately, many of these concepts and skills can be understood by even young children but, unfortunately, most teachers are not conversant with them. Teachers should first learn the concepts and skills themselves.

11. Develop Skills of Creative Problem-Solving. Productive independent study requires a great deal of creative problem-solving. In my own undergraduate and graduate classes and in workshops and institutes I have conducted, I have found that most teachers at all levels of education are greatly deficient in the basic skills of creative problem-solving.

In a number of other sources I have outlined in some detail how I think teachers can acquire these skills.[9, 10, 11] Generally,

[9] E. Paul Torrance, "Creativity in the Classroom," *Instructor*, 1964–65, 74. (A series of ten articles.)

[10] Torrance, *Rewarding Creative Behavior, op. cit.*

[11] E. Paul Torrance, "Nurture of Creative Talents," *Theory into Practice*, October 1967, 5, 168–174.

I have suggested that teachers in a particular building join together in a year-long series of workshops to help one another practice and improve these professional skills. Such skills can be acquired only by practice, deliberate effort, and intelligent and imaginative use of feedback about progress.

WHAT FACTORS ARE RELEVANT TO ITS IMPACT?

To reap—and continue to reap—the value of independent study as an instructional tool, we must acquire additional information about a variety of factors relevant to its impact. Some of the more pressing questions are those related to the ability of students who can make use of independent study, the kinds of content that lend themselves to this instructional approach, and the exact teaching styles that are most favorable to it. At the present time, we do not have firm information concerning any of these questions.

Does Ability Matter?   Except in a few more or less accidental cases, provisions for independent study have traditionally been limited to high-achieving students of superior ability. Apparently, however, this practice has not proved to be very satisfactory. Many high-ability students require a great deal of structure and have developed habits that make it difficult for them to learn through independent study. It is also highly likely that many students who could make excellent use of independent study are overlooked when high previous achievement and measured intelligence are the criteria of selection. Tests of creative thinking ability, a life experience inventory, or a questionnaire to measure preference for structured or open-ended learning situations would probably be more effective in selecting students for special programs of independent study. Since it is quite likely that these preferences and abilities develop through experience, teachers should give all students some chance for independent study and be alert to interests, potentialities, and motivations that would make independent study successful.

What Should the Content Be?   Almost any subject matter will lend itself to independent study. Some types of subject matter probably lend themselves to it more readily than others, but I do not believe anyone can yet specify which these are.

What Teaching Style?   I do not know of any very direct and rigorous evidence that indicates which teaching style would be most favorable to independent study. I expect that the responsive environment rather than the traditional stimulus-response approach will be the most compatible with such study. Teachers and classrooms should be learner-centered rather than teacher-centered, low-controlling rather than high-controlling, and integrative rather than dominative. The most successful teacher would probably use indirect rather than direct control in a classroom that is characterized by variety, flexibility, openness, activity, problem-solving, inquiry, and experimentation.

And the Community?   It is inevitable that the use of individual study will lead to increased use of the community and learning facilities within the community. Its libraries, museums, institutions, governmental procedures, businesses, and industries will inescapably be brought into the process. When one permits or encourages independent study, he must be prepared to let one thing lead to another. The solution of problems that interest students will surely take them into the community and involve them with people throughout the world.

What Administrative Setting?   A wide range of administrative settings is possible with independent study as an instructional tool. Somehow, however, administrative procedures must provide time and space for it and freedom to take the students outside the school plant itself from time to time. Libraries, laboratories, and special rooms and equipment can be designed for independent study, but they are not essential. Special periods can also be set aside for independent study, or some students may engage in it while others learn in other ways. Finally, while there is a need for order, control, and structure, the administrative setting congenial to independent study must be tolerant of a certain degree of unpredictability and even disorder. It must also have a high tolerance for complexity. If very many students are involved in independent study, then simplicity of administration becomes virtually impossible.

DIFFERENTIATING INSTRUCTION FOR DISADVANTAGED STUDENTS

Daniel U. Levine

Most teachers and administrators believe that instructional practices should be modified in accordance with the needs of students. Attempts to individualize instruction usually include differentiating the content of materials and varying the way materials are presented in the classroom. Attention is sometimes given to more global differences in the ways educational goals can be pursued in a given instructional setting. At one end of a continuum the ideal educational approach can be conceived as the organization of instruction based on and leading to self-directed inquiry. At the other end of the continuum the ideal approach is conceived as the detailed structuring of instruction to accomplish objectives defined with reference to specific subject matter and easily tested skills. Because these approaches represent contending philosophies of education, most educators eventually become committed, emotionally and intellectually, to one or the other. A person with an implicit or an explicit attachment to a pervasive philosophy of education will have trouble recognizing situations in which relatively unambiguous considerations make a competing philosophy more appropriate. In a sense, we are confronted with a dilemma in which our allegiance to a particular

Reprinted from *The Educational Forum*, Vol. 30, January 1966, pp. 143–146, by permission of Kappa Delta Pi, An Honor Society in Education, owners of the copyright.

philosophy (which defines individualized instruction as desirable) interferes with our attempts to individualize instruction by analyzing the advantages and disadvantages of competing approaches in each instructional setting. This dilemma has become most acute in connection with the unusual learning problem of a very special population among our students: those who are socially, economically, and culturally disadvantaged.

There are many possible ways to structure the classroom learning environment. If we are sincere in the belief that no one standard approach is suited to the needs of groups of students differing greatly in previous experience, then we must identify, if only crudely, the particular learning environment which best matches the developmental level and the behavioral characteristics of any given group of students. More specifically, there is good reason to believe that practices which are appropriate in working with middle-class students are inadvisable when working with disadvantaged youngsters. Students who live in underprivileged and disorganized communities need unusually intensive guidance and supervision, so much so, in fact, that classroom approaches almost universally recommended in educational psychology textbooks will not work in inner-city schools. This is not because disadvantaged youngsters are inherently less able than middle-class youngsters to handle the "relaxed" and relatively unstructured classroom atmosphere rightfully extolled in the textbooks, but because child-raising practices in low-income families negate the likelihood that the children of the poor will perform well in such an atmosphere.

Melvin L. Kohn has summarized several of the relevant social class differences in child-rearing values as follows:

. . . working-class parents value obedience, neatness, and cleanliness more highly than do middle-class parents, and . . . middle-class parents in turn value curiosity, happiness, consideration, and—most importantly—self-control more highly than do working-class parents. We further found that there are characteristic clusters of value choice in the two social classes: working-class parental values center on conformity to external proscriptions, middle-class values on *self*-direction. To working-class parents, it is an overt act that matters: the child should not transgress externally imposed rules; to middle-class parents, it is the child's motives and feelings that matter: the child should govern himself.

. . . the differences between middle-class and working-class parental values are probably a function of the entire complex of differences in life conditions characteristics of the two social classes.[1]

Not trained to work in a self-disciplined style which leads to success in a "progressive" classroom, disadvantaged students quickly exceed the boundaries teachers assume pupils will observe as a matter of course. Inexperienced in planning activities directed at long-range goals, disadvantaged youngsters are at sea when teachers attempt to "recognize" their human dignity and individuality by allowing them great discretion in deciding how to proceed in the classroom. Unprepared for situations in which they are asked for preferences rather than told what to do, disadvantaged youngsters are overwhelmed by the freedom imposed by the teacher who has been taught that children respond best when rules and expectations are flexible and self-defined. Such children should not be expected to handle all at once a confusing excess of freedom and the terrifying range of choice which is its necessary corollary. They are likely to respond more satisfactorily to regularity and pattern in classroom activities. Definite rules should be introduced and enforced at the very beginning of the school year. The teacher should stand ready to provide close direction at every stage, no matter how small, of each classroom activity.

Assignments and learning activities necessarily will be more

[1] Melvin L. Kohn, "Social Class and Parent-Child Relationships: An Interpretation," in Frank Riessman, Jerome Cohen, and Arthur Pearl (Eds.), *Mental Health of the Poor* (New York: Macmillan, 1964), pp. 163, 165.

highly structured in classrooms serving disadvantaged students than in classrooms constituted by pupils who have been encouraged at home to seek independence and self-direction. The structuring of learning experiences fortunately does not require that pupils be excluded from participation in the definition of rules or that teachers be any less fair and sympathetic or assignments and presentations any less imaginative than is desirable in all classrooms; attention to these instructional goals is as important, if not more important, in inner-city schools than in schools serving more fortunate youngsters.

The long-range goals in working with disadvantaged youth are, of course, identical to those to which we are committed elsewhere: to develop students who can think for themselves and who are skilled in the self-directed management of meaningful learning experiences. Such an orientation is developed slowly, by degrees, even with children whose environment includes every educational advantage parents can provide. It is unrealistic and, indeed, harmful to expect the children of poverty to meet such an expectation before they have been exposed to many years of carefully supervised instruction which gradually liberates their undeveloped capacity to study and to learn.

At the present time inner-city classrooms organized to provide highly structured and clearly patterned activities congruent with the special circumstances and problems of disadvantaged students are difficult to find. Typically, the inner-city teacher, with high hopes and admirable motives, attempts to organize her classroom in accordance with the optimistic philosophies expressed in the textbooks used in teacher training courses. The pupils, bewildered by the absence of unsophisticated supervision they are accustomed to expect from adults, thereby are set loose to work their wills. The situation quickly moves beyond the control of the teacher. The teacher and/or the administration proceeds to overcompensate by clamping down with extreme regimentation and heavy-handed discipline. The school itself increasingly resembles a jail, with predictable reactions from its inmates. As a consequence, gradual growth in self-control is unlikely to take place among the pupils.

Whether many inner-city schools introduce the highly structured learning experiences most appropriate in working with disadvantaged youngsters will depend on the strength and resolution of administrators and teachers. The pressures of public opinion are likely to favor the implementation of less suitable policies. Public opinion concerning education, after all, is primarily middle-class opinion. The demands middle-class parents will make of the schools during the next few years are fairly predictable. As more and more students begin to compete for openings in the nation's colleges, pressure on elementary and secondary school personnel to tolerate no "nonsense" in the classroom will grow still more stringent. More middle-class parents will accept the seemingly reasonable idea that instruction be organized so as to reward only unusually distinguished achievement, hoping of course that this will produce a ticket of admission to college for their son or daughter. In an elitist atmosphere generated by a pervasive concern for college preparation, it will be easy to lose sight of motivation, inquiry, and individualized instructional arrangements for disadvantaged students as legitimate concerns in the public schools.

A growing minority of middle-class parents, however, will support an opposite position favoring the elimination of school practices which make their school-age children tense and overburdened. As the crisis over college enrollment intensifies, parents whose children are only average in ability cannot afford the "luxury" of any policy they believe might somehow lower academic standards in their local school; therefore parents enlisting in the "reduce the pressures" camp will be mainly those whose children are unusually high in ability and initial motivation to learn. In the past year a trend toward the publication in influential newspapers and periodicals of articles critical of extreme competition for grades and of the increasing quantity of homework assigned in high-prestige schools has already become evident.[2] Since the advocacy of an across-the-board relaxation of school requirements coincides with the personal views of many teachers and administrators, educators will be tempted to manipulate the support of this influential segment of public opinion to reverse the current retreat from the free and easy classroom atmosphere recommended in the "progressive" philosophy of education. Such a retrenchment is desirable in schools populated mainly by middle-class students; the obvious danger is that inner-city schools, too, will be swept along and recommitted to the relatively unstructured organization of learning experiences which has proved disastrous in teaching students from disadvantaged communities.

The polar pressures generated by warring middle-class factions are unlikely to contribute to the synthesis of instructional arrangements appropriate to the needs of working-class children. Neither an overwhelming dedication to preparation for college (viewed as the simple-minded accretion of factual information) nor a rededication to emotional equilibrium of the child (viewed as liberation from control imposed by adults) is likely to produce the complicated interweaving of firm yet sympathetic supervision, imaginative subject matter, variety in the ways materials are presented, regularity and consistency in the scheduling and conduct of learning experiences, and strong emphasis on the development of basic learning skills which is needed to stimulate improved academic performance from disadvantaged students. Initiative in plan-

---

[2] Washington journalist William S. White, for example, recently devoted a column to the heavy load imposed on his teen-age daughter. He pointed out that while adults increasingly treasure and guard their leisure time, school requirements systematically deprive students of the time for constructive non-school activities.

ning and implementing an educational philosophy specifically directed at the needs of disadvantaged youngsters can be carried out only by professionals who understand what is at stake and have the courage to insist that it deserves the highest priority.

REPORT ANALYSIS: CHILDREN AND THEIR PRIMARY SCHOOLS*

Joseph Featherstone

The Plowden Report consists of two very fat volumes containing something like half a million words, and to focus on any one of its concerns would be misleading. But there is one aspect of the report that is gaining particular attention in Britain and America. The report stands for a certain style of primary education, for a set of ideas behind classroom practices now spreading throughout England. American readers who thread their way through the relevant sections of this massive official document will discover some of the foundations for a new way of thinking about what a good primary school should be like, involving different and, to American eyes, radical conceptions of the role of the teacher, teaching strategies, the organization of the classroom, children's learning, how the school day should proceed, and the nature of a proper curriculum for primary school children.

The report testifies to the fact that many British teachers and principals are coming to think of a good school as one in which children are trained to work for the most part independently, in an environment thoughtfully laid out to permit

* Central Advisory Council on Education, *Children and Their Primary Schools:* Volume I, *The Report;* Volume II, *Research and Surveys* (London: H.M.S.O., 1967).

Joseph Featherstone, "Report Analysis: Children and Their Primary Schools," *Harvard Educational Review*, 38 (Spring 1968), pp. 317–328. Copyright © 1968 by President and Fellows of Harvard College.

choices from an array of materials—water, clay, pets, practical math apparatus, science stuff, all kinds of books for individual reading, private dictionaries and word books, free-writing notebooks, powder paint and easels, puppet theaters, and play houses. Teachers and children in some schools are given choices to such an extent that there is no longer a fixed curriculum or a set timetable. (This is called, variously, the free or integrated day.) Children move freely around the classroom at their tasks and within limits they are encouraged to talk to each other. In the sort of informal class praised by the Plowden Committee, the teacher is less the generating force in learning and more the catalyst, or consultant, for the activities of individual children or small groups. Teachers walk around, give advice, listen, diagnose, and set the pace of things, but they don't try to take over the job of learning from the children. Thus a number of schools are confirming in practice what theorists have often maintained: children have extraordinary powers of learning, and they frequently learn best from their own activities.

At the end of Part Four of the report, "The Structure of Primary Education," there are three splendid vignettes of visits to schools run along these lines; since they give a vivid sense of what the report is advocating, I'll quote one at some length:

The first is an infant school occupying a 70 year old building, three storeys high, near the station in a large city. The visitor, if he is a man, will attract a great deal of attention from the children, some of whom will try to 'make a corner in him.' He may even receive a proposal in marriage from one of the girls. This has nothing to do with his personal charms, but it is a sure sign of a background of inadequate or absentee fathers. A number of children are coloured, and some of the white children are poorly dressed. All, however, are clean. The children seem to be using every bit of the building (the top floor is sealed off) and its surroundings. They spread into the hall, the corridors, and the playground. The nursery class has its own quarters, and the children are playing with sand, water, paint, clay, dolls, rocking horses and big push toys under the supervision of their teacher. This is how they learn. There is serenity in the room, belying the belief that happy children are always noisy. The children make rather a mess of themselves and their room but this, with a little help, they clear up themselves. A dispute between two little boys about who is to play with what is resòlved by the teacher. . . . Learning is going on all the time, but there is not much direct teaching.

Going out into the playground, the visitor finds a group of children, with their teacher, clustered round a large square box full of earth. The excitement is all about an earthworm, which none of the children had ever seen before. Their classroom door opens on to the playground and inside are the rest of the class, seated at tables disposed informally about the room, some reading books that they have themselves chosen from the copious shelves along the side of the room, and some measuring the quantities of water that different vessels will hold. Soon the teacher and worm watchers return except for two children who have gone up to the library to find a book on worms and the class begins to tidy up in preparation for lunch. The visitor's attention is attracted by the paintings on the wall, and, as he looks at them, he is soon joined by a number of children who volunteer information about them. In a moment the preparations for lunch are interrupted as the children press forward with things they have painted, or written, or constructed. . . .

Later in the day, the visitor finds a small group of six and seven year olds who are writing about the music they have enjoyed with the headmistress. He picks up a home-made book entitled 'My book of sounds' and reads the following, written on plain unlined paper:

> 'The mandolin is made with lovely soft smooth wood and it has a pattern like tortoise shell on it. It has pearl on it and it is called mother of pearl. It has eight strings and they are all together in twos and all the pairs make a different noise. The ones with the thickest strings make the lowest notes and the ones that have the thinnest strings make the highest notes. When I put the mandolin in my lap and I pulled the thickest string it kept on for a long time and I pulled the thinnest wire and it did not last so long and I stroked them all and they didn't go away for a long time.'

Quite a number of these children write with equal fluency and expressiveness, and with concentration. The sound of music from the hall attracts the visitor and there he finds a class who are making up and performing a dance drama in which the forces of good are overcoming the forces of evil to the accompaniment of drums and tambourines. . . . (pp. 103–4)

American visitors to England, including myself, have been deeply impressed by similar schools; they have reported that the quality of work in the best of them—particularly in written expression, art, and the ability of the children to reason mathematically—is better than the quality of work in the best American schools. (And a few first-rate English schools serve poor children.)

Rumors and mutters of all this were beginning to spread to this country. It was only last year, however, with the publication of the Plowden Report, that Americans could appreciate the scope of the changes taking place. For it is now clear from this stately hymn of praise to informal classes that the English are on their way toward establishing certain conditions for good learning on a fairly large, national scale. There are twenty-three thousand primary schools in England. By the report's standards of judgment, which are discernible, if not very precise, 109 of them are outstanding in quality, and about 10 per cent are outstanding in some respect—math, art, "movement," children's writing, or whatever. In all, the report estimates that one-third of the country's schools are quite clearly good. There is nothing dogmatic about the Plowen Report, and it is quite willing to grant that some formal schools give a good education. But the report is promoting a trend, and it strongly implies that most of its good third are proceeding along informal lines. Of the remaining English schools, it says a third are somewhat affected by the changes taking place, and another third are scarcely touched at all, still frozen into rigid patterns of teaching and learning.

This is certainly impressive, although it would be easy to exaggerate the extent of change. England is not yet a primary school teacher's utopia. Salaries are wretched, classes everywhere are overcrowded, schools receive pittances for books and equipment, buildings are often Gothic horrors, and the prospects for stable reform are constantly eroded by an appalling turnover of teaching staff. Throughout the country the spread of informal practices is extremely uneven, and the quality of schools working along free lines varies enormously. The best work is done in a handful of local authorities. It would be a fair guess that most of the 109 outstanding schools the report cites are in places that have conspicuously led the way in primary education: Bristol, the West Riding of York-shire, Leicestershire, and Oxfordshire. There are plenty of authorities still sunk in the ice age, and a morbid American could track down many schools, particularly in immigrant areas, that are failing in exactly the ways our slum schools are failing.

In addition, Americans have to remember that the trans-formation from formal to informal teaching is most wide-spread—most revolutionary—in the "infant" schools, which take children between the ages of five and seven (in some cases eight), teaching them to read and write and work with num-bers. In the "junior" schools, which take children from seven or eight to eleven or twelve, change is slower. Junior schools in leading authorities are playing dazzling variations on the free themes developed by the infant schools but, in general, education at the junior level is still fairly conventional and very much in the shadow of standard tests and inflexible secondary schools. Junior school teachers need to build up their confidence that free methods can work—which means, among other things, developing the backlog of experience, traditions, and materials that infant teachers now possess. Whether they will succeed on the scale of the infant schools is an open question.

There is no doubt that Americans are intrigued by the suc-cesses of the good English schools. Word of English practices comes at a moment when many people are questioning our rigid assumptions about children's learning, particularly the learning of young children. And curiously enough, after a decade of more or less useful innovation, there is still a great pedagogical vacuum. Reforms have come and gone, but no-body has really addressed himself to teachers who desperately lack practical alternatives to our present formal methods of

teaching. Parents and teachers are starved for concrete examples of what a good classroom might look like, and what
it would be like to do a good job. It is therefore altogether
natural that Americans have so far concentrated on the external features of English classrooms: the rich stores of
materials, often home-made, for children to handle and play
with; the variety of activities going on at the same time; the
absorption of children in their tasks; the freedom permitted
children and teachers; the altered role of teachers in an informal setting; the constant use of hallways, playgrounds, and
space that is wasted in most school buildings; the curriculum
that arises in large part from the interests and doings of children (in the sketch I quoted, the earthworm, or the dancing
formations of good against evil).

In some ways this specific focus has been all too the good.
We badly need descriptions of what actually happens in good
classes. For too long, talk about education in this country has
been divorced from what children and teachers really do. But
while this is true, and while any account of a real classroom
may seem like an oasis in the great American desert of educational discourse, there is also some danger that Americans will
see only the surfaces of the great transformation in British
schools, without trying to understand the settings in which
change is happening, or the spirit behind the enterprise. We
need many more detailed vignettes and scenarios of teachers
and children in action, but we must also develop an appreciation for the prerequisites for these sorts of classes. It is neither
possible nor desirable to transplant British practices whole to
American soil, but examining the preconditions for this kind
of good learning may suggest things that we have done badly
and things that we have left undone in our attempts to make
American schools better, more humane, and more capable of
treating people as individuals.

It seems to me that there are three general sets of questions
for which we need answers:

1. The first has to do with very specific accounts of informal classes, materials, mechanics, what teachers do, and even homely details such as housekeeping, and the ways in which English teachers avoid chaos. We have made a start on this, although there is still much to be done.
2. The second involve finding out how this change has happened, the prerequisities for such a reform.
3. And a third set of questions goes beyond the kinds of questions we normally ask to explore how we would go about making sensible qualitative distinctions between informal classes that are merely adequate and those that are outstanding.

Being in the midst of everything, the British have not been able to do more than offer some answers to the first set of questions. They take the contexts of change pretty much for granted and they are often unaware of the setting in which they work. For example, only a brief historical sketch is presented in the Plowden Report (Chapter 16). Nor have the British pursued the report's tantalizing distinctions between outstanding and merely good schools, or between good and bad schools.

Here then is a tentative agenda of the things both British and American educators will need to know in order to answer my second set of questions:

1. We must find out more about the traditions of the infant schools. Their separate existence was a historical accident, but surely a necessary prerequisite for the development of informal methods was the idea that smaller children have distinct needs. As separate institutions, the infant schools were free to experiment; furthermore, nursery and infant teachers were often trained together, and this meant that English teachers have for some time been inclined to relate their teaching to basic theories of child development stressing individual learning and learning in what David Hawkins calls

the concrete mode—messing around with stuff. The characteristic innovations of the primary school revolution were first worked out in a small number of infant schools much influenced by practices in nursery schools run by followers of Montessori, Susan Isaacs, Dewey, and Piaget. Now, in good junior schools, individual learning and concrete materials are proving to be appropriate for older children, too, although the materials may have to be much more complex. This profound influence of nursery and kindergarten education on the practices of later grades is just the opposite of what has happened in this country, where good preschools have often been bullied into becoming prep schools for inflexible first-grade classes.

2. We also need to study very carefully the relationship between theory and practice in the English schools. I suspect that this whole matter is much more complicated than we usually think. It is quite clear, for instance, that developmental psychology, and particularly the work of Piaget, is used to provide theoretical justification for some of the methods of the infant and good junior schools. The fusion of developmental theory and classroom practice is easiest to see in the area of mathematics where certain assumptions—such as the idea that young children need to build up layers of experience before they can master abstractions—are beginning to pervade classrooms and even shape the direction of further innovation. Part Two of the Plowden Report, "The Growth of the Child," shows this theoretical influence at work in its impressive arguments for the proposition that each child develops at a separate pace. And even when the report is simply examining the practices of good schools, it points out that they correspond to a definite view of teaching:

It lays special stress on individual discovery, on first hand experience, and on opportunities for creative work. It insists that knowledge does not fall in nearly separate compartments, and that work and play are not opposite, but complementary. (p. 187).

Yet while a body of intertwined psychological and pedagogical theory may be emerging in England, it is important to note what the Plowden Report emphasizes: that heads and teachers in schools most successful in practice are often unable to formulate their aims clearly and convincingly. What they do is the result of personal experiences in the classroom; their view of children's learning is worked out in practice, over time, and it is not a matter of applying abstract theorems.

This is an important lesson for Americans, and a difficult one to learn in the absence of living examples of good informal classes. Theory matters, but we know very little about learning and the nature of small children, and theory can only be useful where it has a live relationship with children and teachers in actual classrooms. Without this relationship, theories are sterile. Piaget is a good example of this. Whether or not his work comes to be generally accepted, he has pushed English teachers in sound pedagogical directions. His influence is creative, even though it would be easy to interpret him in a doctrinaire fashion and use his theories to justify all sorts of absurd practices. By contrast, John Dewey's influence in America in the days before he became unfashionable turned out to be largely uncreative, of little or no practical use to working teachers. The difference, I think, is not only a matter of what the two men have to say. Piaget is fortunate in that there are many teachers in England whose work is already on the fringes of what he is getting at. This is something for educational academics to ponder.

3. Closely related both to the spread of infant school practices and to the implications of developmental theory is another phenomenon: the reluctance of some primary school heads and teachers to let crude quantitative standards, such as IQ and standard test scores, determine the education of small children (however much they may accept them for older students). In a few good authorities there is a decline in the practice of "streaming," or ability grouping, which most American teachers and many British teachers still see as a necessary evil. The Plowden Report notes that in classes where the emphasis is on individual, rather than group learn-

ing, teachers have found that they can do without tracking. With the blessings of the Report, more and more infant schools are abandoning ability grouping, and it is increasingly common for junior schools in good authorities to stop tracking in the first two years and in a few cases the third. The British educational system has traditionally laid great emphasis on tracking, and no one knows whether this trend can continue to make headway in the schools dealing with older children. (A tiny number of schools are even doing away with age grouping as an unreliable guide: they are introducing "family," or "vertical" grouping, mixing children of different ages in the same classroom. This seems to work especially well in the early years of school when experienced children help teach newcomers.)

Another manifestation of this same reluctance to let unreliable quantitative standards determine educational decisions is the decline of the "eleven-plus" examination in a few leading authorities. The pressure against change has eased most in the authorities that have successfully abolished this examination which used to settle the academic fate of English children at the age of eleven. The abolition of this wasteful practice has, for obvious reasons, helped the chances for reform in the junior schools.

Some further perspective on testing is clearly necessary for understanding the English reform: A survey in Volume Two of the Plowden Report shows that on measurable achievement in conventional tests, children in formal classes do slightly better than children in informal classes. The difference is greatest in mechanical arithmetic and least in reading. (There is some evidence that these differences disappear in later school years.) This is scarcely surprising. Formal schools teach children to take tests; that is their function, and it would be astounding if all their efforts didn't produce some results. In view of the lack of test training in freer schools, the surprise is that their test results are so high. The math taught in informal schools (mathematical relationships, in which the process of thought counts for more than arithmetical skill), and the English (free writing instead of grammar and so on) put students at an obvious disadvantage on standard achievement tests. England and America badly need new kinds of tests, to be sure, but the point to reflect on is whether people in this country are ready to accept standards other than the ones we now use. The quality of work in the better informal schools *is* incredibly good by standards that are fairly measurable, and there are few reading problems; but it is profoundly significant that English teachers do not defend their methods as better ways to learn the three R's. They defend them simply as more appropriate to the ways in which children think and grow. This is what seems so extraordinary to an American, that teachers and parents can accept the notion that there are many values to be gained through schooling. In the uncertainties of the American educational scene, the tendency now is always to look for specific results, narrowly defined and hence readily measurable. Whether we can bring ourselves to accept other standards will have a great deal to do with whether informal methods can flourish here.

4. Another line of inquiry we must pursue is the nature of curriculum reform in England. Part Five of the Plowden Report, in many ways the heart of the document, emphasizes the development of a new conception of a curriculum: as I noted, much of what goes on in good schools stems from the interests and activities of individual children, and not some fixed notion of what has to be taught. What is particularly interesting is the way in which patterns of individual learning have developed in one subject—in one period of a formal school day— and then spread to others. For some British schools as early as the '30's, art was the first subject in which children were encouraged to choose the content of their work. Others began with individual "movement" and mime and interpretive dancing in their PE classes instead of calisthenics. Some introduced the musical instruments devised for children by the composer, Carl Orff.

Of all subjects, two have conspicuously flowered in the last decade. The first is free writing, literature produced by children on subjects of their own choosing ranging from autobiographical sketches and poetry to elegant writings on science and math. And the second is mathematics, which has recently become the single most important catalyst for schools making the transition from formal to informal teaching. (Plowden estimates that between 10 and 20 per cent of the primary schools have substantially altered their ways of teaching math along individual and concrete lines.) Here the excellent work of the English curriculum projects, the Nuffield Foundation and the Schools Council, has been important. In sharp contrast to American projects which are in the hands of university people and other specialists remote from life in the classroom, the British are taking great pains to enlist classroom teachers in the process of creating and spreading new ideas and materials. One of the most significant aspects of the changes in England is that, in all cases, working teachers have been major contributors to reform. In fact, curriculum projects are just catching up to teachers in first-rate schools, and the best materials are often simply arrangements and codifications of the practices of good classes—teacher's handbooks, filled with practical suggestions and reproductions of work that children have actually done, not canned lessons.

There are also wider, more murky aspects of curriculum reform that we need to look into: for example, one British teacher suggested to me that classes of forty students and over in an atmosphere receptive to experiments stimulate teachers to make instruction more individual. Another teacher wondered whether the lack of money for large-scale projects in England hasn't goaded teachers to do more on their own.

5. These speculations may or may not be on the right track, but they at least point to a crucial precondition for reform: the large measure of autonomy granted principals and teachers within the decentralized English educational system. This relative autonomy affects the quality of all relationships within

the system. Furthermore, British schools traditionally feel reasonably secure from pressures of parental and public opinion. This has some bearing on their readiness to experiment but my own guess is that freedom for teachers and principals within the walls of a school is more important than freedom from interference on the part of parents. Parents seem to approve of the new methods when they understand them, for one thing. And for another, some educators and critics such as the sociologist Michael Young argue that the remoteness of English schools from parents is a serious educational problem, especially in schools dealing with poor children. (A survey finding in Volume Two of Plowden supports this view although the report's discussion of community schooling has little to add to the lively American debate over parent participation and community schools.)

6. The relative freedom of teachers and principals is one of the most important elements in the reform, but by itself it was not sufficient. There is another element that seems to be equally important, although we in America have very little understanding of how it works. This is the emergence of a class of people whose precise function is vague and hard to describe. The archetype of the class, although perhaps not its most influential members, are the HMI's, the government inspectors, who in recent years have stopped playing the role of educational policemen in charge of enforcing standards and instead have become advisors, agents for disseminating change and identifying good schools and willing teachers. In what is perhaps an even more important departure, local authorities have set up similar groups, either formally or informally: In some cases the work of local inspectors has taken on an advisory character, and a few exceptional authorities have set up advisory offices with teams of teachers whose sole responsibilities are to encourage and train other teachers and interest them in trying out new ideas. In some places heads of schools seem to fill the advisory role; there are infinite variations.

What we Americans learn about the setting for reform from pursuing these questions may be fairly disheartening. For instance, the last two preconditions are glaringly absent from the American landscape. Our teachers do not have freedom, and we have nothing resembling the various kinds of advisors. Nor if advisory centers were set up in American school systems tomorrow would we have enough teachers able to handle the role, people with plenty of informal teaching experience and skilled at the art of helping other people without bossing them around. Even the English are having trouble locating such talent. If we develop good informal classes, we will also have to develop ways of spotting potential advisors, since they are probably essential for any kind of widespread reform.

Answering my third set of questions may require that we develop a different way of looking at teaching and writing about it. Specific qualitative concerns—such as what makes a good teacher or a good school—are lacking in most of our discussions of education, as are specific accounts of children learning. Partly this reflects the general staff mentality of our reformers, who tend to think on a grandiose and therefore hollow scale, and who are not really interested in pedagogy anyway, and partly it reflects the influence of the kind of quantitative social science that now dominates educational discourse. Last year's Coleman Report marked the beginning of a great advance in knowledge, but it is characteristic of our prevailing cast of thought that Mr. Coleman and his colleagues were not particularly interested in doing qualitative studies of individual schools that worked—for instance, black schools whose pupils were unexpectedly scoring very well on the tests. With due respect for the kind of research now going on, I think it unlikely that we will find out much about how good schools succeed by continuing to submit relatively crude data to increasingly refined statistical manipulation.

Here I think the unevenness of the English reform is a piece of luck for us. There are plenty of schools in the middle of the painful process of trying to reform themselves; and there are undoubtedly schools that have made a fearful botch of informal teaching. We have a lot to learn by studying both. One aspect of developing our thinking along more qualitative lines will involve doing pathology of schools that fail, as well as anatomy of schools that succeed brilliantly. Another will involve finding out what makes 109 schools in England superb, and why other schools doing the same things don't match up. Often, as David Hawkins has noted, you visit a school in England where the materials and organization seem to be there, but where the teacher is merely coping, managing the room well enough without particularly responding to individual children. Frequently, though not always, such classes are still better than most of our formal classes, but they should not be confused with those classes in which the teacher is watching closely and knows when to intervene or change the pace or make a demand for the greatest pedagogical advantage. Among many other things, the reform in the English schools provides us with a chance to get a better idea of that mysterious thing, good teaching.

The Plowden Report has one other lesson: the undogmatic tone it adopts, and its general modesty. What it favors is perfectly clear, but it readily concedes that there are many roads to heaven. A good formal class is often better than a poor informal one, and what teachers do, the motions they go through—the integrated day, or whatever—counts for less than what they are, and whether they can respect children. Modesty, in particular, would seem a desirable virtue for Americans to practice, for surely the progress of English schools is a standing rebuke to our whole system of educational research, the vast and costly apparatus we have erected to generate misinformation about children. Why have we done so little practical work relevant to working teachers on finding out the conditions for good learning? And how, after all these years, have we remained ignorant of the extent to which small children can take the initiative in learning? These are shameful questions.